D1597312

Money Does Grow On Trees

Set In Soul

© 2020 Tatiana Media LLC in partnership with Set In Soul LLC

ISBN #: 978-1-949874-92-1

Published by Tatiana Media LLC

All rights reserved. No part of this journal/publication may be reproduced, stored in a retrieval system, or transmitted in any form or by any means, electronic, mechanical, photocopying, recording, scanning, or otherwise, except as permitted under Section 107 or 108 of the 1976 United States Copyright Act whatsoever without express written permission from the author, except in the case of brief quotations embodied in critical articles and reviews. Please refer all pertinent questions to the publisher.

Limit of Liability/Disclaimer of Warranty: While the publisher and author have used their best efforts in preparing this book/journal, they make no representations or warranties with respect to the accuracy or completeness of the contents of this book/journal and specifically disclaim any implied warranties. The advice and strategies contained herein may not be suitable for your situation. You should consult with a professional where appropriate. Neither the publisher nor author shall be liable for any loss of profit or any other emotional, physical, spiritual and mental distress and damages, including but not limited to special, incidental, consequential, or other damages.

For general information on our other products and services, please contact our Customer Support within the United States at support@setinsoul.com.

Tatiana Media LLC as well as Set In Soul LLC publishes its books in a variety of electronic formats. Some content that appears in print may not be available in electronic books.

This Journal Belongs To

_____

Dedicated To Everyone Willing To Create Their Own Reality. You Will Never Lack.

Table Of Contents

How To Use This Journal

A dream is a wish your heart makes
When you're fast asleep
In dreams you will lose your heartaches
Whatever you wish for, you keep

Have faith in your dreams and someday
Your rainbow will come smiling through
No matter how your heart is grieving
If you keep on believing
The dream that you wish will come true

- A Dream Is A Wish Your Heart Makes By Lily James in Cinderella

These lyrics just feel good. That is how you want to feel …. good about money. If you have dreams that include money but have a mediocre to bad relationship with money, then this journal is here to help you establish a better relationship with it. It's time to let go of whatever negative beliefs you have about money. Maybe your negative beliefs stem from what you have heard other people say about money, past experiences, or any actions/losses that gave you a reason to reject that any amount of money belongs to you. What you should know is that you tell money what to do, not the other way around. You should also know that you can manifest any amount of money you want into your life. Believe it and it is yours. Now what do you think is blocking you from having a great relationship with what is suppose to work for you? Whatever your answer is, you will be breaking down those beliefs and expanding your mind with this journal by spending billions. Yes billions. We do not care if you do not need the billions, we want you to have it and spend it easily. We want you to believe that it is yours. Don't want to spend billions? Okay then, spend trillions. This is your money tree. We want you to know that money does grow on trees and they grow easily on trees. Your trees. Your tree is ready to blossom and just needs more attention from you.

With this journal you will be expanding your beliefs. You will be imagining and having fun with your money. No longer will you feel stress or lack. You are to feel abundant. The feeling of financial abundance is not to be a temporary feeling for you but one that keeps on flowing. Think of this journal as your constant companion throughout your journey in growing your money tree.

Every morning and every night you are to fill out the prompts in this journal that are designed to help you play around with your money. There are also sections in this journal that are titled 'Today's Money Story' where you are to create ways that you have received money, gave money, etc. This journal is also here for you to explore how money affects a majority of your senses and how you react to it. You will be surprised by what you reveal to yourself about how you really feel about money. It is with this journal you will demolish your feelings on lack and expand your thoughts on giving. Once you start breaking some undeserving thoughts, you will then start getting rid of the weeds and fungus preventing your money tree from growing. Have fun and manifest. Have fun and manifest. Again have fun and manifest because money does grow on your tree.

Releasing Old Thoughts To Now Creating New Money Beliefs

Releasing Old Thoughts To Now Creating New Money Beliefs

I Would Describe My Relationship With Money:

What Do I Believe Money Represents?

What About Money Excites Me?

What About Money Scares Me?

What Do I Blame On Money?

Releasing Old Thoughts To Now Creating New Money Beliefs

What Do I Want Money To Do For Me?

Where Does Money Come From?

I View Money:

I Have Seen Money Make People:

How Have I Limited Myself From Getting Money?

Releasing Old Thoughts To Now Creating New Money Beliefs

I Believe Money Is:

Money Makes Me Feel:

When I Have Money, I:

When I Have Money, I Feel:

When I Do Not Have Money, I:

Releasing Old Thoughts To Now Creating New Money Beliefs

When I Do Not Have Money, I Feel:

People Around Me Who Have Money:

How Do People Around Me Get Money?

What Do The People Around Me With Money Believe?

What Has Money Changed For Me?

Releasing Old Thoughts To Now Creating New Money Beliefs

What Will Having More Money Change For Me?

Not Having Enough Money Has Caused:

What Have People Around Me Always Said About Money?

How Have I Gotten Money In The Past?

How Would I Like To Get Money In The Future?

Releasing Old Thoughts To Now Creating New Money Beliefs

How Do I Currently Get Money?

How Would I Like To Feel About Money?

What Would I Do With More Money?

Some Unwanted Thoughts About Money I Would Like To Change:

I Stopped Believing:

Releasing Old Thoughts To Now Creating New Money Beliefs

I Started Believing:

What Is 'Enough' Money?

What Does It Mean To Not Have 'Enough' Money?

What Is 'Too Much' Money?

What Does It Mean To Have 'Too Much' Money?

Releasing Old Thoughts To Now Creating New Money Beliefs

Have I Ever Had 'Too Much' Money?

Spending Money Makes Me Feel:

Bills Make Me Feel:

I Want To Experience:

What Is The Purpose Of Money?

Releasing Old Thoughts To Now Creating New Money Beliefs

Have I Been Working 'FOR' Money?

How Does Money Serve Me?

When Have I Felt The Richest?

The Largest Sum Of Money I Have Ever Had Up To This Point Of My Life At One Time:

The Most Amount Of Money I Have Ever Held In My Hand:

Releasing Old Thoughts To Now Creating New Money Beliefs

The Most Amount Of Money I Plan To Ever Hold In My Hand:

The Most Amount Of Money I Have Ever Spent On Something:

The Most Amount Of Money I Plan To Ever Spend On Something:

The Most Amount Of Money I Have Ever Given To Someone:

The Most Amount Of Money I Plan To Ever Give To Someone:

Releasing Old Thoughts To Now Creating New Money Beliefs

Do I Have An Attachment To Money?

The Best Advice I Have Ever Received About Money:

The Most Useful Information I Have Heard And Applied About Money:

Do I Talk About Money With My Family And/Or Friends?

If I Responded Yes To The Previous Prompt, How Do I Speak About Money (Tone, Attitude ....)?

Releasing Old Thoughts To Now Creating New Money Beliefs

What Do I Want To Believe About Money?

Is It Easy For Me To Imagine Something I Want To Obtain?

Reasons I Have Doubted Myself:

Money Is Stopping Me From:

Money Helped Me To Start:

Releasing Old Thoughts To Now Creating New Money Beliefs

I Imagine Myself:

With Money I Could:

What Is Unrealistic?

What Is Realistic?

I Am Prepared For:

Releasing Old Thoughts To Now Creating New Money Beliefs

What Do I Want To Produce?

How Do I Plan To Elevate My Mentality And Beliefs About Money?

What Am I Willing To Forgive When It Comes To Money?

What Am I Releasing With Old Money Beliefs?

What Thoughts Have I Been Holding On To About Money?

Releasing Old Thoughts To Now Creating New Money Beliefs

I Want To Invest My Money:

Everyday I Want To Spend My Money On:

I Want To Feel Easy About:

I Want To Obtain:

Do I Make It Easy For Money To Flow To Me?

Releasing Old Thoughts To Now Creating New Money Beliefs

If I Responded Yes To The Previous Prompt, How Do I Make It Easy For Money To Flow To Me?

Have I Become A Magnet For Money?

Am I Desperate For Money?

I Have The Power To Change:

I No Longer Limit Myself:

Releasing Old Thoughts To Now Creating New Money Beliefs

I Have Seen Money:

I Am Asking God For:

I Am Now Allowing:

I Am Now Choosing:

I Am Now Letting Go:

Releasing Old Thoughts To Now Creating New Money Beliefs

I Am In A Space:

What Easily Comes To Me?

I Am Making Room For:

What Is Working For Me?

What Will Be Working For Me?

Releasing Old Thoughts To Now Creating New Money Beliefs

Things Are Changing Because:

Money And I Are:

Everyday I Want To Feel:

I No Longer Believe:

There Is Power In Knowing:

Releasing Old Thoughts To Now Creating New Money Beliefs

I Know I Am Able:

What Do I Want?

Can I Have What I Want?

Will I Have What I Want?

I Will Not Feel Guilty About:

Releasing Old Thoughts To Now Creating New Money Beliefs

How Am I Shifting My Focus?

I Am Aligning With:

I Can Change:

I Will Change:

I Have Stopped Stressing Over:

Releasing Old Thoughts To Now Creating New Money Beliefs

I Want More:

I Have More:

I Am:

I Have:

I Feel:

Releasing Old Thoughts To Now Creating New Money Beliefs

I Do Not Lack:

I Am Expecting:

How Hard Is It For Me To Give Someone Money?

Do I Believe I Am Generous?

If I Responded Yes To The Previous Prompt, How Am I Generous?

Releasing Old Thoughts To Now Creating New Money Beliefs

I Give:

What Am I Thankful For?

I Act As If:

I Will Start Acting As If:

For Every Dollar I Spend, I Get Back:

Releasing Old Thoughts To Now Creating New Money Beliefs

In The Past Six Months, What Would I Have Done Differently With Money?

If Given Two Million Dollars Today, How Would I Spend It?

Spending My Billions

Spending My Billions
(Morning Thoughts - See It And Believe It)

Date:

I Feel:

Today's Money Belief:

I Believe God Is:

Today I Am Attracting (Write Down How Much Money You Are Attracting Today):

Today I Am Open To:

How Much Money Do I Plan On Spending Today (Write Down Your Imagined Amount)?

Today I Am Telling My Money To:

Based On My Response To The Previous Prompt, What Am I Spending My Money On?

Today I Am Repeating To Myself:

Today I Am Investing My Money In:

I Feel Good Knowing:

For Every Dollar I Spend, How Much Of It Comes Back To Me?

Morning Thoughts:

Spending My Billions
(Nightly Thoughts - See It And Believe It)

Today I Visualized:

I Am Free From:

Today I Gave Away (Write Down How Much Money You Imagined Giving Away Or Actually Gave Away):

How Much Money Grew On My Money Tree Today?

I Felt Good Holding In My Hand (Write Down The Imagined Dollar Amount):

What Did I Actually Spend My Money On Today?

Today I Created:

How Did It Feel To Spend The Amount Of Money That I Spent Today And Why Did I Feel This Way?

Today It Was Fun To:

Today I Am Grateful For:

Today I Acted As If:

Tonight's Thoughts:

Spending My Billions
(Morning Thoughts - See It And Believe It)

Date:

I Feel:

Today's Money Belief:

I Believe God Is:

Today I Am Attracting (Write Down How Much Money You Are Attracting Today):

Today I Am Open To:

How Much Money Do I Plan On Spending Today (Write Down Your Imagined Amount)?

Today I Am Telling My Money To:

Based On My Response To The Previous Prompt, What Am I Spending My Money On?

Today I Am Repeating To Myself:

Today I Am Investing My Money In:

I Feel Good Knowing:

For Every Dollar I Spend, How Much Of It Comes Back To Me?

Morning Thoughts:

Spending My Billions
(Nightly Thoughts - See It And Believe It)

Today I Visualized:

I Am Free From:

Today I Gave Away (Write Down How Much Money You Imagined Giving Away Or Actually Gave Away):

How Much Money Grew On My Money Tree Today?

I Felt Good Holding In My Hand (Write Down The Imagined Dollar Amount):

What Did I Actually Spend My Money On Today?

Today I Created:

How Did It Feel To Spend The Amount Of Money That I Spent Today And Why Did I Feel This Way?

Today It Was Fun To:

Today I Am Grateful For:

Today I Acted As If:

Tonight's Thoughts:

Today's Money Story

Whatever I Spend Will Come Back To Me One Hundred Times Over.

Spending My Billions
(Morning Thoughts - See It And Believe It)

Date:

Today's Money Belief:

Today I Am Attracting (Write Down How Much Money You Are Attracting Today):

How Much Money Do I Plan On Spending Today (Write Down Your Imagined Amount)?

Based On My Response To The Previous Prompt, What Am I Spending My Money On?

Today I Am Investing My Money In:

For Every Dollar I Spend, How Much Of It Comes Back To Me?

I Feel:

I Believe God Is:

Today I Am Open To:

Today I Am Telling My Money To:

Today I Am Repeating To Myself:

I Feel Good Knowing:

Morning Thoughts:

Spending My Billions

(Nightly Thoughts - See It And Believe It)

Today I Visualized:

I Am Free From:

Today I Gave Away (Write Down How Much Money You Imagined Giving Away Or Actually Gave Away):

How Much Money Grew On My Money Tree Today?

I Felt Good Holding In My Hand (Write Down The Imagined Dollar Amount):

What Did I Actually Spend My Money On Today?

Today I Created:

How Did It Feel To Spend The Amount Of Money That I Spent Today And Why Did I Feel This Way?

Today It Was Fun To:

Today I Am Grateful For:

Today I Acted As If:

Tonight's Thoughts:

My Money Works For Me.

Today's Money Story

Spending My Billions
(Morning Thoughts - See It And Believe It)

Date:

Today's Money Belief:

Today I Am Attracting (Write Down How Much Money You Are Attracting Today):

How Much Money Do I Plan On Spending Today (Write Down Your Imagined Amount)?

Based On My Response To The Previous Prompt, What Am I Spending My Money On?

Today I Am Investing My Money In:

For Every Dollar I Spend, How Much Of It Comes Back To Me?

I Feel:

I Believe God Is:

Today I Am Open To:

Today I Am Telling My Money To:

Today I Am Repeating To Myself:

I Feel Good Knowing:

Morning Thoughts:

Spending My Billions
(Nightly Thoughts - See It And Believe It)

Today I Visualized:

I Am Free From:

Today I Gave Away (Write Down How Much Money You Imagined Giving Away Or Actually Gave Away):

How Much Money Grew On My Money Tree Today?

I Felt Good Holding In My Hand (Write Down The Imagined Dollar Amount):

What Did I Actually Spend My Money On Today?

Today I Created:

How Did It Feel To Spend The Amount Of Money That I Spent Today And Why Did I Feel This Way?

Today It Was Fun To:

Today I Am Grateful For:

Today I Acted As If:

Tonight's Thoughts:

Today's Money Story

Money Mindset Practice

Each Day Write Down 10 Things You Are Grateful That Your Money Does.

I Give My Money Power.

How Would I Spend $100,000?

Spending My Billions
(Morning Thoughts - See It And Believe It)

Date:

Today's Money Belief:

Today I Am Attracting (Write Down How Much Money You Are Attracting Today):

How Much Money Do I Plan On Spending Today (Write Down Your Imagined Amount)?

Based On My Response To The Previous Prompt, What Am I Spending My Money On?

Today I Am Investing My Money In:

For Every Dollar I Spend, How Much Of It Comes Back To Me?

I Feel:

I Believe God Is:

Today I Am Open To:

Today I Am Telling My Money To:

Today I Am Repeating To Myself:

I Feel Good Knowing:

Morning Thoughts:

Spending My Billions
(Nightly Thoughts - See It And Believe It)

Today I Visualized:

I Am Free From:

Today I Gave Away (Write Down How Much Money You Imagined Giving Away Or Actually Gave Away):

How Much Money Grew On My Money Tree Today?

I Felt Good Holding In My Hand (Write Down The Imagined Dollar Amount):

What Did I Actually Spend My Money On Today?

Today I Created:

How Did It Feel To Spend The Amount Of Money That I Spent Today And Why Did I Feel This Way?

Today It Was Fun To:

Today I Am Grateful For:

Today I Acted As If:

Tonight's Thoughts:

Spending My Billions
(Morning Thoughts - See It And Believe It)

Date: | I Feel:

Today's Money Belief: | I Believe God Is:

Today I Am Attracting (Write Down How Much Money You Are Attracting Today): | Today I Am Open To:

How Much Money Do I Plan On Spending Today (Write Down Your Imagined Amount)? | Today I Am Telling My Money To:

Based On My Response To The Previous Prompt, What Am I Spending My Money On? | Today I Am Repeating To Myself:

Today I Am Investing My Money In: | I Feel Good Knowing:

For Every Dollar I Spend, How Much Of It Comes Back To Me? | Morning Thoughts:

Spending My Billions
(Nightly Thoughts - See It And Believe It)

Today I Visualized:

I Am Free From:

Today I Gave Away (Write Down How Much Money You Imagined Giving Away Or Actually Gave Away):

How Much Money Grew On My Money Tree Today?

I Felt Good Holding In My Hand (Write Down The Imagined Dollar Amount):

What Did I Actually Spend My Money On Today?

Today I Created:

How Did It Feel To Spend The Amount Of Money That I Spent Today And Why Did I Feel This Way?

Today It Was Fun To:

Today I Am Grateful For:

Today I Acted As If:

Tonight's Thoughts:

Today's Money Story

I Am Taking Control Of My Situation.

Spending My Billions
(Morning Thoughts - See It And Believe It)

Date:

Today's Money Belief:

Today I Am Attracting (Write Down How Much Money You Are Attracting Today):

How Much Money Do I Plan On Spending Today (Write Down Your Imagined Amount)?

Based On My Response To The Previous Prompt, What Am I Spending My Money On?

Today I Am Investing My Money In:

For Every Dollar I Spend, How Much Of It Comes Back To Me?

I Feel:

I Believe God Is:

Today I Am Open To:

Today I Am Telling My Money To:

Today I Am Repeating To Myself:

I Feel Good Knowing:

Morning Thoughts:

Spending My Billions
(Nightly Thoughts - See It And Believe It)

Today I Visualized:

I Am Free From:

Today I Gave Away (Write Down How Much Money You Imagined Giving Away Or Actually Gave Away):

How Much Money Grew On My Money Tree Today?

I Felt Good Holding In My Hand (Write Down The Imagined Dollar Amount):

What Did I Actually Spend My Money On Today?

Today I Created:

How Did It Feel To Spend The Amount Of Money That I Spent Today And Why Did I Feel This Way?

Today It Was Fun To:

Today I Am Grateful For:

Today I Acted As If:

Tonight's Thoughts:

Money Mindset Practice

Create Your Ideal Money Day.

My Personal Money Thoughts

Spending My Billions
(Morning Thoughts - See It And Believe It)

Date:

Today's Money Belief:

I Feel:

I Believe God Is:

Today I Am Attracting (Write Down How Much Money You Are Attracting Today):

Today I Am Open To:

How Much Money Do I Plan On Spending Today (Write Down Your Imagined Amount)?

Today I Am Telling My Money To:

Based On My Response To The Previous Prompt, What Am I Spending My Money On?

Today I Am Repeating To Myself:

Today I Am Investing My Money In:

I Feel Good Knowing:

For Every Dollar I Spend, How Much Of It Comes Back To Me?

Morning Thoughts:

Spending My Billions
(Nightly Thoughts - See It And Believe It)

Today I Visualized:

I Am Free From:

Today I Gave Away (Write Down How Much Money You Imagined Giving Away Or Actually Gave Away):

How Much Money Grew On My Money Tree Today?

I Felt Good Holding In My Hand (Write Down The Imagined Dollar Amount):

What Did I Actually Spend My Money On Today?

Today I Created:

How Did It Feel To Spend The Amount Of Money That I Spent Today And Why Did I Feel This Way?

Today It Was Fun To:

Today I Am Grateful For:

Today I Acted As If:

Tonight's Thoughts:

Spending My Billions

(Morning Thoughts - See It And Believe It)

Date: I Feel:

Today's Money Belief: I Believe God Is:

Today I Am Attracting (Write Down   Today I Am Open To:
How Much Money You Are Attracting
Today):

How Much Money Do I Plan On   Today I Am Telling My Money To:
Spending Today (Write Down Your
Imagined Amount)?

Based On My Response To The   Today I Am Repeating To Myself:
Previous Prompt, What Am I Spending
My Money On?

Today I Am Investing My Money In: I Feel Good Knowing:

For Every Dollar I Spend, How Much Of   Morning Thoughts:
It Comes Back To Me?

Spending My Billions

(Nightly Thoughts - See It And Believe It)

Today I Visualized:

I Am Free From:

Today I Gave Away (Write Down How Much Money You Imagined Giving Away Or Actually Gave Away):

How Much Money Grew On My Money Tree Today?

I Felt Good Holding In My Hand (Write Down The Imagined Dollar Amount):

What Did I Actually Spend My Money On Today?

Today I Created:

How Did It Feel To Spend The Amount Of Money That I Spent Today And Why Did I Feel This Way?

Today It Was Fun To:

Today I Am Grateful For:

Today I Acted As If:

Tonight's Thoughts:

Today's Money Story

How Would I Spend $1,000,000?

There Is Nothing Wrong With Starting Over.

How Would I Spend $10,000,000?

Spending My Billions
(Morning Thoughts - See It And Believe It)

Date:

I Feel:

Today's Money Belief:

I Believe God Is:

Today I Am Attracting (Write Down How Much Money You Are Attracting Today):

Today I Am Open To:

How Much Money Do I Plan On Spending Today (Write Down Your Imagined Amount)?

Today I Am Telling My Money To:

Based On My Response To The Previous Prompt, What Am I Spending My Money On?

Today I Am Repeating To Myself:

Today I Am Investing My Money In:

I Feel Good Knowing:

For Every Dollar I Spend, How Much Of It Comes Back To Me?

Morning Thoughts:

Spending My Billions
(Nightly Thoughts - See It And Believe It)

Today I Visualized:

I Am Free From:

Today I Gave Away (Write Down How Much Money You Imagined Giving Away Or Actually Gave Away):

How Much Money Grew On My Money Tree Today?

I Felt Good Holding In My Hand (Write Down The Imagined Dollar Amount):

What Did I Actually Spend My Money On Today?

Today I Created:

How Did It Feel To Spend The Amount Of Money That I Spent Today And Why Did I Feel This Way?

Today It Was Fun To:

Today I Am Grateful For:

Today I Acted As If:

Tonight's Thoughts:

Spending My Billions
(Morning Thoughts - See It And Believe It)

Date:

Today's Money Belief:

Today I Am Attracting (Write Down How Much Money You Are Attracting Today):

How Much Money Do I Plan On Spending Today (Write Down Your Imagined Amount)?

Based On My Response To The Previous Prompt, What Am I Spending My Money On?

Today I Am Investing My Money In:

For Every Dollar I Spend, How Much Of It Comes Back To Me?

I Feel:

I Believe God Is:

Today I Am Open To:

Today I Am Telling My Money To:

Today I Am Repeating To Myself:

I Feel Good Knowing:

Morning Thoughts:

Spending My Billions

(Nightly Thoughts - See It And Believe It)

Today I Visualized:

I Am Free From:

Today I Gave Away (Write Down How Much Money You Imagined Giving Away Or Actually Gave Away):

How Much Money Grew On My Money Tree Today?

I Felt Good Holding In My Hand (Write Down The Imagined Dollar Amount):

What Did I Actually Spend My Money On Today?

Today I Created:

How Did It Feel To Spend The Amount Of Money That I Spent Today And Why Did I Feel This Way?

Today It Was Fun To:

Today I Am Grateful For:

Today I Acted As If:

Tonight's Thoughts:

The Goal Is To Live Life On My Own Terms.

I Am A Money Magnet.

Today's Money Story

My Personal Money Thoughts

Spending My Billions
(Morning Thoughts - See It And Believe It)

Date: | I Feel:

Today's Money Belief: | I Believe God Is:

Today I Am Attracting (Write Down How Much Money You Are Attracting Today): | Today I Am Open To:

How Much Money Do I Plan On Spending Today (Write Down Your Imagined Amount)? | Today I Am Telling My Money To:

Based On My Response To The Previous Prompt, What Am I Spending My Money On? | Today I Am Repeating To Myself:

Today I Am Investing My Money In: | I Feel Good Knowing:

For Every Dollar I Spend, How Much Of It Comes Back To Me? | Morning Thoughts:

Spending My Billions
(Nightly Thoughts - See It And Believe It)

Today I Visualized:

I Am Free From:

Today I Gave Away (Write Down How Much Money You Imagined Giving Away Or Actually Gave Away):

How Much Money Grew On My Money Tree Today?

I Felt Good Holding In My Hand (Write Down The Imagined Dollar Amount):

What Did I Actually Spend My Money On Today?

Today I Created:

How Did It Feel To Spend The Amount Of Money That I Spent Today And Why Did I Feel This Way?

Today It Was Fun To:

Today I Am Grateful For:

Today I Acted As If:

Tonight's Thoughts:

Spending My Billions
(Morning Thoughts - See It And Believe It)

Date:

Today's Money Belief:

Today I Am Attracting (Write Down How Much Money You Are Attracting Today):

How Much Money Do I Plan On Spending Today (Write Down Your Imagined Amount)?

Based On My Response To The Previous Prompt, What Am I Spending My Money On?

Today I Am Investing My Money In:

For Every Dollar I Spend, How Much Of It Comes Back To Me?

I Feel:

I Believe God Is:

Today I Am Open To:

Today I Am Telling My Money To:

Today I Am Repeating To Myself:

I Feel Good Knowing:

Morning Thoughts:

Spending My Billions
(Nightly Thoughts - See It And Believe It)

Today I Visualized:

I Am Free From:

Today I Gave Away (Write Down How Much Money You Imagined Giving Away Or Actually Gave Away):

How Much Money Grew On My Money Tree Today?

I Felt Good Holding In My Hand (Write Down The Imagined Dollar Amount):

What Did I Actually Spend My Money On Today?

Today I Created:

How Did It Feel To Spend The Amount Of Money That I Spent Today And Why Did I Feel This Way?

Today It Was Fun To:

Today I Am Grateful For:

Today I Acted As If:

Tonight's Thoughts:

What Is Great About My Life Right Now?

My Personal Money Thoughts

How Would I Spend $100,000,000?

Today's Money Story

Spending My Billions
(Morning Thoughts - See It And Believe It)

Date:

Today's Money Belief:

Today I Am Attracting (Write Down How Much Money You Are Attracting Today):

How Much Money Do I Plan On Spending Today (Write Down Your Imagined Amount)?

Based On My Response To The Previous Prompt, What Am I Spending My Money On?

Today I Am Investing My Money In:

For Every Dollar I Spend, How Much Of It Comes Back To Me?

I Feel:

I Believe God Is:

Today I Am Open To:

Today I Am Telling My Money To:

Today I Am Repeating To Myself:

I Feel Good Knowing:

Morning Thoughts:

Spending My Billions

(Nightly Thoughts - See It And Believe It)

Today I Visualized:

I Am Free From:

Today I Gave Away (Write Down How Much Money You Imagined Giving Away Or Actually Gave Away):

How Much Money Grew On My Money Tree Today?

I Felt Good Holding In My Hand (Write Down The Imagined Dollar Amount):

What Did I Actually Spend My Money On Today?

Today I Created:

How Did It Feel To Spend The Amount Of Money That I Spent Today And Why Did I Feel This Way?

Today It Was Fun To:

Today I Am Grateful For:

Today I Acted As If:

Tonight's Thoughts:

Spending My Billions
(Morning Thoughts - See It And Believe It)

Date:

I Feel:

Today's Money Belief:

I Believe God Is:

Today I Am Attracting (Write Down How Much Money You Are Attracting Today):

Today I Am Open To:

How Much Money Do I Plan On Spending Today (Write Down Your Imagined Amount)?

Today I Am Telling My Money To:

Based On My Response To The Previous Prompt, What Am I Spending My Money On?

Today I Am Repeating To Myself:

Today I Am Investing My Money In:

I Feel Good Knowing:

For Every Dollar I Spend, How Much Of It Comes Back To Me?

Morning Thoughts:

Spending My Billions

(Nightly Thoughts - See It And Believe It)

Today I Visualized:

I Am Free From:

Today I Gave Away (Write Down How Much Money You Imagined Giving Away Or Actually Gave Away):

How Much Money Grew On My Money Tree Today?

I Felt Good Holding In My Hand (Write Down The Imagined Dollar Amount):

What Did I Actually Spend My Money On Today?

Today I Created:

How Did It Feel To Spend The Amount Of Money That I Spent Today And Why Did I Feel This Way?

Today It Was Fun To:

Today I Am Grateful For:

Today I Acted As If:

Tonight's Thoughts:

Today's Money Story

Money Mindset Practice

Create A Money Meditation. Spend 17 Minutes Every Morning And Night In Your Money Meditation.

Everyday I Wake Up Trusting The Process.

I Am Staying Focused.

Spending My Billions
(Morning Thoughts - See It And Believe It)

Date:

Today's Money Belief:

Today I Am Attracting (Write Down How Much Money You Are Attracting Today):

How Much Money Do I Plan On Spending Today (Write Down Your Imagined Amount)?

Based On My Response To The Previous Prompt, What Am I Spending My Money On?

Today I Am Investing My Money In:

For Every Dollar I Spend, How Much Of It Comes Back To Me?

I Feel:

I Believe God Is:

Today I Am Open To:

Today I Am Telling My Money To:

Today I Am Repeating To Myself:

I Feel Good Knowing:

Morning Thoughts:

Spending My Billions
(Nightly Thoughts - See It And Believe It)

Today I Visualized:

I Am Free From:

Today I Gave Away (Write Down How Much Money You Imagined Giving Away Or Actually Gave Away):

How Much Money Grew On My Money Tree Today?

I Felt Good Holding In My Hand (Write Down The Imagined Dollar Amount):

What Did I Actually Spend My Money On Today?

Today I Created:

How Did It Feel To Spend The Amount Of Money That I Spent Today And Why Did I Feel This Way?

Today It Was Fun To:

Today I Am Grateful For:

Today I Acted As If:

Tonight's Thoughts:

My Personal Money Thoughts

Today's Money Story

Spending My Billions

(Morning Thoughts - See It And Believe It)

Date:

I Feel:

Today's Money Belief:

I Believe God Is:

Today I Am Attracting (Write Down How Much Money You Are Attracting Today):

Today I Am Open To:

How Much Money Do I Plan On Spending Today (Write Down Your Imagined Amount)?

Today I Am Telling My Money To:

Based On My Response To The Previous Prompt, What Am I Spending My Money On?

Today I Am Repeating To Myself:

Today I Am Investing My Money In:

I Feel Good Knowing:

For Every Dollar I Spend, How Much Of It Comes Back To Me?

Morning Thoughts:

Spending My Billions

(Nightly Thoughts - See It And Believe It)

Today I Visualized:

I Am Free From:

Today I Gave Away (Write Down How Much Money You Imagined Giving Away Or Actually Gave Away):

How Much Money Grew On My Money Tree Today?

I Felt Good Holding In My Hand (Write Down The Imagined Dollar Amount):

What Did I Actually Spend My Money On Today?

Today I Created:

How Did It Feel To Spend The Amount Of Money That I Spent Today And Why Did I Feel This Way?

Today It Was Fun To:

Today I Am Grateful For:

Today I Acted As If:

Tonight's Thoughts:

How Would I Spend

$1,000,000,000.00?

My Personal Money Thoughts

Spending My Billions
(Morning Thoughts - See It And Believe It)

Date:

Today's Money Belief:

Today I Am Attracting (Write Down How Much Money You Are Attracting Today):

How Much Money Do I Plan On Spending Today (Write Down Your Imagined Amount)?

Based On My Response To The Previous Prompt, What Am I Spending My Money On?

Today I Am Investing My Money In:

For Every Dollar I Spend, How Much Of It Comes Back To Me?

I Feel:

I Believe God Is:

Today I Am Open To:

Today I Am Telling My Money To:

Today I Am Repeating To Myself:

I Feel Good Knowing:

Morning Thoughts:

Spending My Billions

(Nightly Thoughts - See It And Believe It)

Today I Visualized:

I Am Free From:

Today I Gave Away (Write Down How Much Money You Imagined Giving Away Or Actually Gave Away):

How Much Money Grew On My Money Tree Today?

I Felt Good Holding In My Hand (Write Down The Imagined Dollar Amount):

What Did I Actually Spend My Money On Today?

Today I Created:

How Did It Feel To Spend The Amount Of Money That I Spent Today And Why Did I Feel This Way?

Today It Was Fun To:

Today I Am Grateful For:

Today I Acted As If:

Tonight's Thoughts:

Today's Money Story

God Guide My Hands And My Feet.

Spending My Billions
(Morning Thoughts - See It And Believe It)

Date:

Today's Money Belief:

Today I Am Attracting (Write Down How Much Money You Are Attracting Today):

How Much Money Do I Plan On Spending Today (Write Down Your Imagined Amount)?

Based On My Response To The Previous Prompt, What Am I Spending My Money On?

Today I Am Investing My Money In:

For Every Dollar I Spend, How Much Of It Comes Back To Me?

I Feel:

I Believe God Is:

Today I Am Open To:

Today I Am Telling My Money To:

Today I Am Repeating To Myself:

I Feel Good Knowing:

Morning Thoughts:

Spending My Billions

(Nightly Thoughts - See It And Believe It)

Today I Visualized:

I Am Free From:

Today I Gave Away (Write Down How Much Money You Imagined Giving Away Or Actually Gave Away):

How Much Money Grew On My Money Tree Today?

I Felt Good Holding In My Hand (Write Down The Imagined Dollar Amount):

What Did I Actually Spend My Money On Today?

Today I Created:

How Did It Feel To Spend The Amount Of Money That I Spent Today And Why Did I Feel This Way?

Today It Was Fun To:

Today I Am Grateful For:

Today I Acted As If:

Tonight's Thoughts:

Spending My Billions

(Morning Thoughts - See It And Believe It)

Date:

I Feel:

Today's Money Belief:

I Believe God Is:

Today I Am Attracting (Write Down How Much Money You Are Attracting Today):

Today I Am Open To:

How Much Money Do I Plan On Spending Today (Write Down Your Imagined Amount)?

Today I Am Telling My Money To:

Based On My Response To The Previous Prompt, What Am I Spending My Money On?

Today I Am Repeating To Myself:

Today I Am Investing My Money In:

I Feel Good Knowing:

For Every Dollar I Spend, How Much Of It Comes Back To Me?

Morning Thoughts:

Spending My Billions

(Nightly Thoughts - See It And Believe It)

Today I Visualized:

I Am Free From:

Today I Gave Away (Write Down How Much Money You Imagined Giving Away Or Actually Gave Away):

How Much Money Grew On My Money Tree Today?

I Felt Good Holding In My Hand (Write Down The Imagined Dollar Amount):

What Did I Actually Spend My Money On Today?

Today I Created:

How Did It Feel To Spend The Amount Of Money That I Spent Today And Why Did I Feel This Way?

Today It Was Fun To:

Today I Am Grateful For:

Today I Acted As If:

Tonight's Thoughts:

Today's Money Story

I Do Not Fear Money.

Spending My Billions
(Morning Thoughts - See It And Believe It)

Date:

I Feel:

Today's Money Belief:

I Believe God Is:

Today I Am Attracting (Write Down How Much Money You Are Attracting Today):

Today I Am Open To:

How Much Money Do I Plan On Spending Today (Write Down Your Imagined Amount)?

Today I Am Telling My Money To:

Based On My Response To The Previous Prompt, What Am I Spending My Money On?

Today I Am Repeating To Myself:

Today I Am Investing My Money In:

I Feel Good Knowing:

For Every Dollar I Spend, How Much Of It Comes Back To Me?

Morning Thoughts:

Spending My Billions
(Nightly Thoughts - See It And Believe It)

Today I Visualized:

I Am Free From:

Today I Gave Away (Write Down How Much Money You Imagined Giving Away Or Actually Gave Away):

How Much Money Grew On My Money Tree Today?

I Felt Good Holding In My Hand (Write Down The Imagined Dollar Amount):

What Did I Actually Spend My Money On Today?

Today I Created:

How Did It Feel To Spend The Amount Of Money That I Spent Today And Why Did I Feel This Way?

Today It Was Fun To:

Today I Am Grateful For:

Today I Acted As If:

Tonight's Thoughts:

Today's Money Story

I Tell My Money What To Do And Where To Go.

Spending My Billions
(Morning Thoughts - See It And Believe It)

Date:

Today's Money Belief:

Today I Am Attracting (Write Down How Much Money You Are Attracting Today):

How Much Money Do I Plan On Spending Today (Write Down Your Imagined Amount)?

Based On My Response To The Previous Prompt, What Am I Spending My Money On?

Today I Am Investing My Money In:

For Every Dollar I Spend, How Much Of It Comes Back To Me?

I Feel:

I Believe God Is:

Today I Am Open To:

Today I Am Telling My Money To:

Today I Am Repeating To Myself:

I Feel Good Knowing:

Morning Thoughts:

Spending My Billions
(Nightly Thoughts - See It And Believe It)

Today I Visualized:

I Am Free From:

Today I Gave Away (Write Down How Much Money You Imagined Giving Away Or Actually Gave Away):

How Much Money Grew On My Money Tree Today?

I Felt Good Holding In My Hand (Write Down The Imagined Dollar Amount):

What Did I Actually Spend My Money On Today?

Today I Created:

How Did It Feel To Spend The Amount Of Money That I Spent Today And Why Did I Feel This Way?

Today It Was Fun To:

Today I Am Grateful For:

Today I Acted As If:

Tonight's Thoughts:

My Personal Money Thoughts

Money Mindset Practice

Write Down 10 Positive Things You Believe You Can Do With Money For Others.

Five People I Will Give Money To (And Write Down How Much)....

1.

2.

3.

4.

5.

Today's Money Story

Spending My Billions
(Morning Thoughts - See It And Believe It)

Date:

Today's Money Belief:

Today I Am Attracting (Write Down How Much Money You Are Attracting Today):

How Much Money Do I Plan On Spending Today (Write Down Your Imagined Amount)?

Based On My Response To The Previous Prompt, What Am I Spending My Money On?

Today I Am Investing My Money In:

For Every Dollar I Spend, How Much Of It Comes Back To Me?

I Feel:

I Believe God Is:

Today I Am Open To:

Today I Am Telling My Money To:

Today I Am Repeating To Myself:

I Feel Good Knowing:

Morning Thoughts:

Spending My Billions

(Nightly Thoughts - See It And Believe It)

Today I Visualized:

I Am Free From:

Today I Gave Away (Write Down How Much Money You Imagined Giving Away Or Actually Gave Away):

How Much Money Grew On My Money Tree Today?

I Felt Good Holding In My Hand (Write Down The Imagined Dollar Amount):

What Did I Actually Spend My Money On Today?

Today I Created:

How Did It Feel To Spend The Amount Of Money That I Spent Today And Why Did I Feel This Way?

Today It Was Fun To:

Today I Am Grateful For:

Today I Acted As If:

Tonight's Thoughts:

Spending My Billions
(Morning Thoughts - See It And Believe It)

Date:

Today's Money Belief:

Today I Am Attracting (Write Down How Much Money You Are Attracting Today):

How Much Money Do I Plan On Spending Today (Write Down Your Imagined Amount)?

Based On My Response To The Previous Prompt, What Am I Spending My Money On?

Today I Am Investing My Money In:

For Every Dollar I Spend, How Much Of It Comes Back To Me?

I Feel:

I Believe God Is:

Today I Am Open To:

Today I Am Telling My Money To:

Today I Am Repeating To Myself:

I Feel Good Knowing:

Morning Thoughts:

Spending My Billions
(Nightly Thoughts - See It And Believe It)

Today I Visualized:

I Am Free From:

Today I Gave Away (Write Down How Much Money You Imagined Giving Away Or Actually Gave Away):

How Much Money Grew On My Money Tree Today?

I Felt Good Holding In My Hand (Write Down The Imagined Dollar Amount):

What Did I Actually Spend My Money On Today?

Today I Created:

How Did It Feel To Spend The Amount Of Money That I Spent Today And Why Did I Feel This Way?

Today It Was Fun To:

Today I Am Grateful For:

Today I Acted As If:

Tonight's Thoughts:

Today's Money Story

Money Is No Longer My Problem.

Spending My Billions
(Morning Thoughts - See It And Believe It)

Date:

Today's Money Belief:

Today I Am Attracting (Write Down How Much Money You Are Attracting Today):

How Much Money Do I Plan On Spending Today (Write Down Your Imagined Amount)?

Based On My Response To The Previous Prompt, What Am I Spending My Money On?

Today I Am Investing My Money In:

For Every Dollar I Spend, How Much Of It Comes Back To Me?

I Feel:

I Believe God Is:

Today I Am Open To:

Today I Am Telling My Money To:

Today I Am Repeating To Myself:

I Feel Good Knowing:

Morning Thoughts:

Spending My Billions

(Nightly Thoughts - See It And Believe It)

Today I Visualized:

I Am Free From:

Today I Gave Away (Write Down How Much Money You Imagined Giving Away Or Actually Gave Away):

How Much Money Grew On My Money Tree Today?

I Felt Good Holding In My Hand (Write Down The Imagined Dollar Amount):

What Did I Actually Spend My Money On Today?

Today I Created:

How Did It Feel To Spend The Amount Of Money That I Spent Today And Why Did I Feel This Way?

Today It Was Fun To:

Today I Am Grateful For:

Today I Acted As If:

Tonight's Thoughts:

Spending My Billions
(Morning Thoughts - See It And Believe It)

Date:

Today's Money Belief:

Today I Am Attracting (Write Down How Much Money You Are Attracting Today):

How Much Money Do I Plan On Spending Today (Write Down Your Imagined Amount)?

Based On My Response To The Previous Prompt, What Am I Spending My Money On?

Today I Am Investing My Money In:

For Every Dollar I Spend, How Much Of It Comes Back To Me?

I Feel:

I Believe God Is:

Today I Am Open To:

Today I Am Telling My Money To:

Today I Am Repeating To Myself:

I Feel Good Knowing:

Morning Thoughts:

Spending My Billions
(Nightly Thoughts - See It And Believe It)

Today I Visualized:

I Am Free From:

Today I Gave Away (Write Down How Much Money You Imagined Giving Away Or Actually Gave Away):

How Much Money Grew On My Money Tree Today?

I Felt Good Holding In My Hand (Write Down The Imagined Dollar Amount):

What Did I Actually Spend My Money On Today?

Today I Created:

How Did It Feel To Spend The Amount Of Money That I Spent Today And Why Did I Feel This Way?

Today It Was Fun To:

Today I Am Grateful For:

Today I Acted As If:

Tonight's Thoughts:

Today's Money Story

My Personal Money Thoughts

Spending My Billions
(Morning Thoughts - See It And Believe It)

Date:

Today's Money Belief:

Today I Am Attracting (Write Down How Much Money You Are Attracting Today):

How Much Money Do I Plan On Spending Today (Write Down Your Imagined Amount)?

Based On My Response To The Previous Prompt, What Am I Spending My Money On?

Today I Am Investing My Money In:

For Every Dollar I Spend, How Much Of It Comes Back To Me?

I Feel:

I Believe God Is:

Today I Am Open To:

Today I Am Telling My Money To:

Today I Am Repeating To Myself:

I Feel Good Knowing:

Morning Thoughts:

Spending My Billions
(Nightly Thoughts - See It And Believe It)

Today I Visualized:

I Am Free From:

Today I Gave Away (Write Down How Much Money You Imagined Giving Away Or Actually Gave Away):

How Much Money Grew On My Money Tree Today?

I Felt Good Holding In My Hand (Write Down The Imagined Dollar Amount):

What Did I Actually Spend My Money On Today?

Today I Created:

How Did It Feel To Spend The Amount Of Money That I Spent Today And Why Did I Feel This Way?

Today It Was Fun To:

Today I Am Grateful For:

Today I Acted As If:

Tonight's Thoughts:

My Mindset Is Improving.

I Am Doing Things Differently.

I Told My Money To Create Opportunities. It Listened.

Ten Feelings I Want To Feel When It Comes To Money....

1.

2.

3.

4.

5.

6.

7.

8.

9.

10.

Spending My Billions
(Morning Thoughts - See It And Believe It)

Date:

Today's Money Belief:

Today I Am Attracting (Write Down How Much Money You Are Attracting Today):

How Much Money Do I Plan On Spending Today (Write Down Your Imagined Amount)?

Based On My Response To The Previous Prompt, What Am I Spending My Money On?

Today I Am Investing My Money In:

For Every Dollar I Spend, How Much Of It Comes Back To Me?

I Feel:

I Believe God Is:

Today I Am Open To:

Today I Am Telling My Money To:

Today I Am Repeating To Myself:

I Feel Good Knowing:

Morning Thoughts:

Spending My Billions
(Nightly Thoughts - See It And Believe It)

Today I Visualized:

I Am Free From:

Today I Gave Away (Write Down How Much Money You Imagined Giving Away Or Actually Gave Away):

How Much Money Grew On My Money Tree Today?

I Felt Good Holding In My Hand (Write Down The Imagined Dollar Amount):

What Did I Actually Spend My Money On Today?

Today I Created:

How Did It Feel To Spend The Amount Of Money That I Spent Today And Why Did I Feel This Way?

Today It Was Fun To:

Today I Am Grateful For:

Today I Acted As If:

Tonight's Thoughts:

Spending My Billions
(Morning Thoughts - See It And Believe It)

Date:

Today's Money Belief:

Today I Am Attracting (Write Down How Much Money You Are Attracting Today):

How Much Money Do I Plan On Spending Today (Write Down Your Imagined Amount)?

Based On My Response To The Previous Prompt, What Am I Spending My Money On?

Today I Am Investing My Money In:

For Every Dollar I Spend, How Much Of It Comes Back To Me?

I Feel:

I Believe God Is:

Today I Am Open To:

Today I Am Telling My Money To:

Today I Am Repeating To Myself:

I Feel Good Knowing:

Morning Thoughts:

Spending My Billions

(Nightly Thoughts - See It And Believe It)

Today I Visualized:

I Am Free From:

Today I Gave Away (Write Down How Much Money You Imagined Giving Away Or Actually Gave Away):

How Much Money Grew On My Money Tree Today?

I Felt Good Holding In My Hand (Write Down The Imagined Dollar Amount):

What Did I Actually Spend My Money On Today?

Today I Created:

How Did It Feel To Spend The Amount Of Money That I Spent Today And Why Did I Feel This Way?

Today It Was Fun To:

Today I Am Grateful For:

Today I Acted As If:

Tonight's Thoughts:

Then He Touched Their Eyes, Saying, "According To Your Faith Let It Be To You."

– Matthew 9:29

Today's Money Story

I Can Be And Do Whatever It Is I Want.

It Does Not Matter What Happened In The Past. The Only Thing That Matters Is What Is Happening Today.

Spending My Billions
(Morning Thoughts - See It And Believe It)

Date:

Today's Money Belief:

Today I Am Attracting (Write Down How Much Money You Are Attracting Today):

How Much Money Do I Plan On Spending Today (Write Down Your Imagined Amount)?

Based On My Response To The Previous Prompt, What Am I Spending My Money On?

Today I Am Investing My Money In:

For Every Dollar I Spend, How Much Of It Comes Back To Me?

I Feel:

I Believe God Is:

Today I Am Open To:

Today I Am Telling My Money To:

Today I Am Repeating To Myself:

I Feel Good Knowing:

Morning Thoughts:

Spending My Billions
(Nightly Thoughts - See It And Believe It)

Today I Visualized:

I Am Free From:

Today I Gave Away (Write Down How Much Money You Imagined Giving Away Or Actually Gave Away):

How Much Money Grew On My Money Tree Today?

I Felt Good Holding In My Hand (Write Down The Imagined Dollar Amount):

What Did I Actually Spend My Money On Today?

Today I Created:

How Did It Feel To Spend The Amount Of Money That I Spent Today And Why Did I Feel This Way?

Today It Was Fun To:

Today I Am Grateful For:

Today I Acted As If:

Tonight's Thoughts:

Today's Money Story

And Do Not Be Conformed To This World, But Be Transformed By The Renewing Of Your Mind, That You May Prove What Is That Good And Acceptable And Perfect Will Of God.

– Romans 12:2

Spending My Billions

(Morning Thoughts - See It And Believe It)

Date:

I Feel:

Today's Money Belief:

I Believe God Is:

Today I Am Attracting (Write Down How Much Money You Are Attracting Today):

Today I Am Open To:

How Much Money Do I Plan On Spending Today (Write Down Your Imagined Amount)?

Today I Am Telling My Money To:

Based On My Response To The Previous Prompt, What Am I Spending My Money On?

Today I Am Repeating To Myself:

Today I Am Investing My Money In:

I Feel Good Knowing:

For Every Dollar I Spend, How Much Of It Comes Back To Me?

Morning Thoughts:

Spending My Billions
(Nightly Thoughts - See It And Believe It)

Today I Visualized:

I Am Free From:

Today I Gave Away (Write Down How Much Money You Imagined Giving Away Or Actually Gave Away):

How Much Money Grew On My Money Tree Today?

I Felt Good Holding In My Hand (Write Down The Imagined Dollar Amount):

What Did I Actually Spend My Money On Today?

Today I Created:

How Did It Feel To Spend The Amount Of Money That I Spent Today And Why Did I Feel This Way?

Today It Was Fun To:

Today I Am Grateful For:

Today I Acted As If:

Tonight's Thoughts:

I Can Do This.

Today's Money Story

Spending My Billions

(Morning Thoughts - See It And Believe It)

Date:

I Feel:

Today's Money Belief:

I Believe God Is:

Today I Am Attracting (Write Down How Much Money You Are Attracting Today):

Today I Am Open To:

How Much Money Do I Plan On Spending Today (Write Down Your Imagined Amount)?

Today I Am Telling My Money To:

Based On My Response To The Previous Prompt, What Am I Spending My Money On?

Today I Am Repeating To Myself:

Today I Am Investing My Money In:

I Feel Good Knowing:

For Every Dollar I Spend, How Much Of It Comes Back To Me?

Morning Thoughts:

Spending My Billions
(Nightly Thoughts - See It And Believe It)

Today I Visualized:

I Am Free From:

Today I Gave Away (Write Down How Much Money You Imagined Giving Away Or Actually Gave Away):

How Much Money Grew On My Money Tree Today?

I Felt Good Holding In My Hand (Write Down The Imagined Dollar Amount):

What Did I Actually Spend My Money On Today?

Today I Created:

How Did It Feel To Spend The Amount Of Money That I Spent Today And Why Did I Feel This Way?

Today It Was Fun To:

Today I Am Grateful For:

Today I Acted As If:

Tonight's Thoughts:

Spending My Billions
(Morning Thoughts - See It And Believe It)

Date:

Today's Money Belief:

Today I Am Attracting (Write Down How Much Money You Are Attracting Today):

How Much Money Do I Plan On Spending Today (Write Down Your Imagined Amount)?

Based On My Response To The Previous Prompt, What Am I Spending My Money On?

Today I Am Investing My Money In:

For Every Dollar I Spend, How Much Of It Comes Back To Me?

I Feel:

I Believe God Is:

Today I Am Open To:

Today I Am Telling My Money To:

Today I Am Repeating To Myself:

I Feel Good Knowing:

Morning Thoughts:

156

Spending My Billions
(Nightly Thoughts - See It And Believe It)

Today I Visualized:

I Am Free From:

Today I Gave Away (Write Down How Much Money You Imagined Giving Away Or Actually Gave Away):

How Much Money Grew On My Money Tree Today?

I Felt Good Holding In My Hand (Write Down The Imagined Dollar Amount):

What Did I Actually Spend My Money On Today?

Today I Created:

How Did It Feel To Spend The Amount Of Money That I Spent Today And Why Did I Feel This Way?

Today It Was Fun To:

Today I Am Grateful For:

Today I Acted As If:

Tonight's Thoughts:

The Money I Have Now....

I Pray For It And Then I Go Out And Get It Because I Expect It.

Spending My Billions

(Morning Thoughts - See It And Believe It)

Date:

I Feel:

Today's Money Belief:

I Believe God Is:

Today I Am Attracting (Write Down How Much Money You Are Attracting Today):

Today I Am Open To:

How Much Money Do I Plan On Spending Today (Write Down Your Imagined Amount)?

Today I Am Telling My Money To:

Based On My Response To The Previous Prompt, What Am I Spending My Money On?

Today I Am Repeating To Myself:

Today I Am Investing My Money In:

I Feel Good Knowing:

For Every Dollar I Spend, How Much Of It Comes Back To Me?

Morning Thoughts:

Spending My Billions

(Nightly Thoughts - See It And Believe It)

Today I Visualized:

I Am Free From:

Today I Gave Away (Write Down How Much Money You Imagined Giving Away Or Actually Gave Away):

How Much Money Grew On My Money Tree Today?

I Felt Good Holding In My Hand (Write Down The Imagined Dollar Amount):

What Did I Actually Spend My Money On Today?

Today I Created:

How Did It Feel To Spend The Amount Of Money That I Spent Today And Why Did I Feel This Way?

Today It Was Fun To:

Today I Am Grateful For:

Today I Acted As If:

Tonight's Thoughts:

Today's Money Story

I Am Rich.

Spending My Billions
(Morning Thoughts - See It And Believe It)

Date:

Today's Money Belief:

Today I Am Attracting (Write Down How Much Money You Are Attracting Today):

How Much Money Do I Plan On Spending Today (Write Down Your Imagined Amount)?

Based On My Response To The Previous Prompt, What Am I Spending My Money On?

Today I Am Investing My Money In:

For Every Dollar I Spend, How Much Of It Comes Back To Me?

I Feel:

I Believe God Is:

Today I Am Open To:

Today I Am Telling My Money To:

Today I Am Repeating To Myself:

I Feel Good Knowing:

Morning Thoughts:

Spending My Billions
(Nightly Thoughts - See It And Believe It)

Today I Visualized:

I Am Free From:

Today I Gave Away (Write Down How Much Money You Imagined Giving Away Or Actually Gave Away):

How Much Money Grew On My Money Tree Today?

I Felt Good Holding In My Hand (Write Down The Imagined Dollar Amount):

What Did I Actually Spend My Money On Today?

Today I Created:

How Did It Feel To Spend The Amount Of Money That I Spent Today And Why Did I Feel This Way?

Today It Was Fun To:

Today I Am Grateful For:

Today I Acted As If:

Tonight's Thoughts:

I Am My Own Gold Mine.

Today's Money Story

Spending My Billions
(Morning Thoughts - See It And Believe It)

Date:

Today's Money Belief:

Today I Am Attracting (Write Down How Much Money You Are Attracting Today):

How Much Money Do I Plan On Spending Today (Write Down Your Imagined Amount)?

Based On My Response To The Previous Prompt, What Am I Spending My Money On?

Today I Am Investing My Money In:

For Every Dollar I Spend, How Much Of It Comes Back To Me?

I Feel:

I Believe God Is:

Today I Am Open To:

Today I Am Telling My Money To:

Today I Am Repeating To Myself:

I Feel Good Knowing:

Morning Thoughts:

Spending My Billions

(Nightly Thoughts - See It And Believe It)

Today I Visualized:

I Am Free From:

Today I Gave Away (Write Down How Much Money You Imagined Giving Away Or Actually Gave Away):

How Much Money Grew On My Money Tree Today?

I Felt Good Holding In My Hand (Write Down The Imagined Dollar Amount):

What Did I Actually Spend My Money On Today?

Today I Created:

How Did It Feel To Spend The Amount Of Money That I Spent Today And Why Did I Feel This Way?

Today It Was Fun To:

Today I Am Grateful For:

Today I Acted As If:

Tonight's Thoughts:

Spending My Billions
(Morning Thoughts - See It And Believe It)

Date: | I Feel:

Today's Money Belief: | I Believe God Is:

Today I Am Attracting (Write Down How Much Money You Are Attracting Today): | Today I Am Open To:

How Much Money Do I Plan On Spending Today (Write Down Your Imagined Amount)? | Today I Am Telling My Money To:

Based On My Response To The Previous Prompt, What Am I Spending My Money On? | Today I Am Repeating To Myself:

Today I Am Investing My Money In: | I Feel Good Knowing:

For Every Dollar I Spend, How Much Of It Comes Back To Me? | Morning Thoughts:

Spending My Billions
(Nightly Thoughts - See It And Believe It)

Today I Visualized:

I Am Free From:

Today I Gave Away (Write Down How Much Money You Imagined Giving Away Or Actually Gave Away):

How Much Money Grew On My Money Tree Today?

I Felt Good Holding In My Hand (Write Down The Imagined Dollar Amount):

What Did I Actually Spend My Money On Today?

Today I Created:

How Did It Feel To Spend The Amount Of Money That I Spent Today And Why Did I Feel This Way?

Today It Was Fun To:

Today I Am Grateful For:

Today I Acted As If:

Tonight's Thoughts:

I Attract Money Everyday.

There Is A Difference Between Who I Am Right Now And Who I Want To Be.

Spending My Billions
(Morning Thoughts - See It And Believe It)

Date:

Today's Money Belief:

Today I Am Attracting (Write Down How Much Money You Are Attracting Today):

How Much Money Do I Plan On Spending Today (Write Down Your Imagined Amount)?

Based On My Response To The Previous Prompt, What Am I Spending My Money On?

Today I Am Investing My Money In:

For Every Dollar I Spend, How Much Of It Comes Back To Me?

I Feel:

I Believe God Is:

Today I Am Open To:

Today I Am Telling My Money To:

Today I Am Repeating To Myself:

I Feel Good Knowing:

Morning Thoughts:

Spending My Billions
(Nightly Thoughts - See It And Believe It)

Today I Visualized:

I Am Free From:

Today I Gave Away (Write Down How Much Money You Imagined Giving Away Or Actually Gave Away):

How Much Money Grew On My Money Tree Today?

I Felt Good Holding In My Hand (Write Down The Imagined Dollar Amount):

What Did I Actually Spend My Money On Today?

Today I Created:

How Did It Feel To Spend The Amount Of Money That I Spent Today And Why Did I Feel This Way?

Today It Was Fun To:

Today I Am Grateful For:

Today I Acted As If:

Tonight's Thoughts:

Spending My Billions
(Morning Thoughts - See It And Believe It)

Date:

Today's Money Belief:

Today I Am Attracting (Write Down How Much Money You Are Attracting Today):

How Much Money Do I Plan On Spending Today (Write Down Your Imagined Amount)?

Based On My Response To The Previous Prompt, What Am I Spending My Money On?

Today I Am Investing My Money In:

For Every Dollar I Spend, How Much Of It Comes Back To Me?

I Feel:

I Believe God Is:

Today I Am Open To:

Today I Am Telling My Money To:

Today I Am Repeating To Myself:

I Feel Good Knowing:

Morning Thoughts:

Spending My Billions
(Nightly Thoughts - See It And Believe It)

Today I Visualized:

I Am Free From:

Today I Gave Away (Write Down How Much Money You Imagined Giving Away Or Actually Gave Away):

How Much Money Grew On My Money Tree Today?

I Felt Good Holding In My Hand (Write Down The Imagined Dollar Amount):

What Did I Actually Spend My Money On Today?

Today I Created:

How Did It Feel To Spend The Amount Of Money That I Spent Today And Why Did I Feel This Way?

Today It Was Fun To:

Today I Am Grateful For:

Today I Acted As If:

Tonight's Thoughts:

Today's Money Story

I Am Abundant. I Live In Abundance.

I Will Always Have More Than What I Need.

Abundance Means....

Abundant Thinking Means....

Spending My Billions
(Morning Thoughts - See It And Believe It)

Date:

Today's Money Belief:

Today I Am Attracting (Write Down How Much Money You Are Attracting Today):

How Much Money Do I Plan On Spending Today (Write Down Your Imagined Amount)?

Based On My Response To The Previous Prompt, What Am I Spending My Money On?

Today I Am Investing My Money In:

For Every Dollar I Spend, How Much Of It Comes Back To Me?

I Feel:

I Believe God Is:

Today I Am Open To:

Today I Am Telling My Money To:

Today I Am Repeating To Myself:

I Feel Good Knowing:

Morning Thoughts:

Spending My Billions

(Nightly Thoughts - See It And Believe It)

Today I Visualized:

I Am Free From:

Today I Gave Away (Write Down How Much Money You Imagined Giving Away Or Actually Gave Away):

How Much Money Grew On My Money Tree Today?

I Felt Good Holding In My Hand (Write Down The Imagined Dollar Amount):

What Did I Actually Spend My Money On Today?

Today I Created:

How Did It Feel To Spend The Amount Of Money That I Spent Today And Why Did I Feel This Way?

Today It Was Fun To:

Today I Am Grateful For:

Today I Acted As If:

Tonight's Thoughts:

Spending My Billions

(Morning Thoughts - See It And Believe It)

Date:

Today's Money Belief:

Today I Am Attracting (Write Down How Much Money You Are Attracting Today):

How Much Money Do I Plan On Spending Today (Write Down Your Imagined Amount)?

Based On My Response To The Previous Prompt, What Am I Spending My Money On?

Today I Am Investing My Money In:

For Every Dollar I Spend, How Much Of It Comes Back To Me?

I Feel:

I Believe God Is:

Today I Am Open To:

Today I Am Telling My Money To:

Today I Am Repeating To Myself:

I Feel Good Knowing:

Morning Thoughts:

Spending My Billions
(Nightly Thoughts - See It And Believe It)

Today I Visualized:

I Am Free From:

Today I Gave Away (Write Down How Much Money You Imagined Giving Away Or Actually Gave Away):

How Much Money Grew On My Money Tree Today?

I Felt Good Holding In My Hand (Write Down The Imagined Dollar Amount):

What Did I Actually Spend My Money On Today?

Today I Created:

How Did It Feel To Spend The Amount Of Money That I Spent Today And Why Did I Feel This Way?

Today It Was Fun To:

Today I Am Grateful For:

Today I Acted As If:

Tonight's Thoughts:

Money Mindset Practice

Create A Money Chant And Set Your Alarm Every 30 Minutes To Recite Your Chant.

Today's Money Story

Spending My Billions
(Morning Thoughts - See It And Believe It)

Date:

I Feel:

Today's Money Belief:

I Believe God Is:

Today I Am Attracting (Write Down How Much Money You Are Attracting Today):

Today I Am Open To:

How Much Money Do I Plan On Spending Today (Write Down Your Imagined Amount)?

Today I Am Telling My Money To:

Based On My Response To The Previous Prompt, What Am I Spending My Money On?

Today I Am Repeating To Myself:

Today I Am Investing My Money In:

I Feel Good Knowing:

For Every Dollar I Spend, How Much Of It Comes Back To Me?

Morning Thoughts:

Spending My Billions
(Nightly Thoughts - See It And Believe It)

Today I Visualized:

I Am Free From:

Today I Gave Away (Write Down How Much Money You Imagined Giving Away Or Actually Gave Away):

How Much Money Grew On My Money Tree Today?

I Felt Good Holding In My Hand (Write Down The Imagined Dollar Amount):

What Did I Actually Spend My Money On Today?

Today I Created:

How Did It Feel To Spend The Amount Of Money That I Spent Today And Why Did I Feel This Way?

Today It Was Fun To:

Today I Am Grateful For:

Today I Acted As If:

Tonight's Thoughts:

Spending My Billions

(Morning Thoughts - See It And Believe It)

Date:

I Feel:

Today's Money Belief:

I Believe God Is:

Today I Am Attracting (Write Down How Much Money You Are Attracting Today):

Today I Am Open To:

How Much Money Do I Plan On Spending Today (Write Down Your Imagined Amount)?

Today I Am Telling My Money To:

Based On My Response To The Previous Prompt, What Am I Spending My Money On?

Today I Am Repeating To Myself:

Today I Am Investing My Money In:

I Feel Good Knowing:

For Every Dollar I Spend, How Much Of It Comes Back To Me?

Morning Thoughts:

Spending My Billions
(Nightly Thoughts - See It And Believe It)

Today I Visualized:

I Am Free From:

Today I Gave Away (Write Down How Much Money You Imagined Giving Away Or Actually Gave Away):

How Much Money Grew On My Money Tree Today?

I Felt Good Holding In My Hand (Write Down The Imagined Dollar Amount):

What Did I Actually Spend My Money On Today?

Today I Created:

How Did It Feel To Spend The Amount Of Money That I Spent Today And Why Did I Feel This Way?

Today It Was Fun To:

Today I Am Grateful For:

Today I Acted As If:

Tonight's Thoughts:

Today's Money Story

My Personal Money Thoughts

My Income Keeps Increasing.

When I See People Who Have What I Want, I....

Spending My Billions
(Morning Thoughts - See It And Believe It)

Date:

Today's Money Belief:

Today I Am Attracting (Write Down How Much Money You Are Attracting Today):

How Much Money Do I Plan On Spending Today (Write Down Your Imagined Amount)?

Based On My Response To The Previous Prompt, What Am I Spending My Money On?

Today I Am Investing My Money In:

For Every Dollar I Spend, How Much Of It Comes Back To Me?

I Feel:

I Believe God Is:

Today I Am Open To:

Today I Am Telling My Money To:

Today I Am Repeating To Myself:

I Feel Good Knowing:

Morning Thoughts:

Spending My Billions
(Nightly Thoughts - See It And Believe It)

Today I Visualized:

I Am Free From:

Today I Gave Away (Write Down How Much Money You Imagined Giving Away Or Actually Gave Away):

How Much Money Grew On My Money Tree Today?

I Felt Good Holding In My Hand (Write Down The Imagined Dollar Amount):

What Did I Actually Spend My Money On Today?

Today I Created:

How Did It Feel To Spend The Amount Of Money That I Spent Today And Why Did I Feel This Way?

Today It Was Fun To:

Today I Am Grateful For:

Today I Acted As If:

Tonight's Thoughts:

Spending My Billions
(Morning Thoughts - See It And Believe It)

Date:

I Feel:

Today's Money Belief:

I Believe God Is:

Today I Am Attracting (Write Down How Much Money You Are Attracting Today):

Today I Am Open To:

How Much Money Do I Plan On Spending Today (Write Down Your Imagined Amount)?

Today I Am Telling My Money To:

Based On My Response To The Previous Prompt, What Am I Spending My Money On?

Today I Am Repeating To Myself:

Today I Am Investing My Money In:

I Feel Good Knowing:

For Every Dollar I Spend, How Much Of It Comes Back To Me?

Morning Thoughts:

Spending My Billions
(Nightly Thoughts - See It And Believe It)

Today I Visualized:

I Am Free From:

Today I Gave Away (Write Down How Much Money You Imagined Giving Away Or Actually Gave Away):

How Much Money Grew On My Money Tree Today?

I Felt Good Holding In My Hand (Write Down The Imagined Dollar Amount):

What Did I Actually Spend My Money On Today?

Today I Created:

How Did It Feel To Spend The Amount Of Money That I Spent Today And Why Did I Feel This Way?

Today It Was Fun To:

Today I Am Grateful For:

Today I Acted As If:

Tonight's Thoughts:

My Personal Money Thoughts

I Attract Money Simply By Being Me.

Spending My Billions
(Morning Thoughts - See It And Believe It)

Date:

Today's Money Belief:

Today I Am Attracting (Write Down
How Much Money You Are Attracting
Today):

How Much Money Do I Plan On
Spending Today (Write Down Your
Imagined Amount)?

Based On My Response To The
Previous Prompt, What Am I Spending
My Money On?

Today I Am Investing My Money In:

For Every Dollar I Spend, How Much Of
It Comes Back To Me?

I Feel:

I Believe God Is:

Today I Am Open To:

Today I Am Telling My Money To:

Today I Am Repeating To Myself:

I Feel Good Knowing:

Morning Thoughts:

Spending My Billions
(Nightly Thoughts - See It And Believe It)

Today I Visualized:

I Am Free From:

Today I Gave Away (Write Down How Much Money You Imagined Giving Away Or Actually Gave Away):

How Much Money Grew On My Money Tree Today?

I Felt Good Holding In My Hand (Write Down The Imagined Dollar Amount):

What Did I Actually Spend My Money On Today?

Today I Created:

How Did It Feel To Spend The Amount Of Money That I Spent Today And Why Did I Feel This Way?

Today It Was Fun To:

Today I Am Grateful For:

Today I Acted As If:

Tonight's Thoughts:

203

Today's Money Story

My Financial Net Worth Is Growing Quickly.

Spending My Billions
(Morning Thoughts - See It And Believe It)

Date:

Today's Money Belief:

Today I Am Attracting (Write Down
How Much Money You Are Attracting
Today):

How Much Money Do I Plan On
Spending Today (Write Down Your
Imagined Amount)?

Based On My Response To The
Previous Prompt, What Am I Spending
My Money On?

Today I Am Investing My Money In:

For Every Dollar I Spend, How Much Of
It Comes Back To Me?

I Feel:

I Believe God Is:

Today I Am Open To:

Today I Am Telling My Money To:

Today I Am Repeating To Myself:

I Feel Good Knowing:

Morning Thoughts:

Spending My Billions
(Nightly Thoughts - See It And Believe It)

Today I Visualized:

I Am Free From:

Today I Gave Away (Write Down How Much Money You Imagined Giving Away Or Actually Gave Away):

How Much Money Grew On My Money Tree Today?

I Felt Good Holding In My Hand (Write Down The Imagined Dollar Amount):

What Did I Actually Spend My Money On Today?

Today I Created:

How Did It Feel To Spend The Amount Of Money That I Spent Today And Why Did I Feel This Way?

Today It Was Fun To:

Today I Am Grateful For:

Today I Acted As If:

Tonight's Thoughts:

Today's Money Story

Money Easily Comes Into My Life And Works For Me.

Spending My Billions
(Morning Thoughts - See It And Believe It)

Date:

Today's Money Belief:

Today I Am Attracting (Write Down How Much Money You Are Attracting Today):

How Much Money Do I Plan On Spending Today (Write Down Your Imagined Amount)?

Based On My Response To The Previous Prompt, What Am I Spending My Money On?

Today I Am Investing My Money In:

For Every Dollar I Spend, How Much Of It Comes Back To Me?

I Feel:

I Believe God Is:

Today I Am Open To:

Today I Am Telling My Money To:

Today I Am Repeating To Myself:

I Feel Good Knowing:

Morning Thoughts:

Spending My Billions
(Nightly Thoughts - See It And Believe It)

Today I Visualized:

I Am Free From:

Today I Gave Away (Write Down How Much Money You Imagined Giving Away Or Actually Gave Away):

How Much Money Grew On My Money Tree Today?

I Felt Good Holding In My Hand (Write Down The Imagined Dollar Amount):

What Did I Actually Spend My Money On Today?

Today I Created:

How Did It Feel To Spend The Amount Of Money That I Spent Today And Why Did I Feel This Way?

Today It Was Fun To:

Today I Am Grateful For:

Today I Acted As If:

Tonight's Thoughts:

I Give Money Away Easily.

I Have Multiple Sources Of Income.

Spending My Billions
(Morning Thoughts - See It And Believe It)

Date:

Today's Money Belief:

Today I Am Attracting (Write Down How Much Money You Are Attracting Today):

How Much Money Do I Plan On Spending Today (Write Down Your Imagined Amount)?

Based On My Response To The Previous Prompt, What Am I Spending My Money On?

Today I Am Investing My Money In:

For Every Dollar I Spend, How Much Of It Comes Back To Me?

I Feel:

I Believe God Is:

Today I Am Open To:

Today I Am Telling My Money To:

Today I Am Repeating To Myself:

I Feel Good Knowing:

Morning Thoughts:

Spending My Billions
(Nightly Thoughts - See It And Believe It)

Today I Visualized:

I Am Free From:

Today I Gave Away (Write Down How Much Money You Imagined Giving Away Or Actually Gave Away):

How Much Money Grew On My Money Tree Today?

I Felt Good Holding In My Hand (Write Down The Imagined Dollar Amount):

What Did I Actually Spend My Money On Today?

Today I Created:

How Did It Feel To Spend The Amount Of Money That I Spent Today And Why Did I Feel This Way?

Today It Was Fun To:

Today I Am Grateful For:

Today I Acted As If:

Tonight's Thoughts:

Spending My Billions
(Morning Thoughts - See It And Believe It)

Date:

Today's Money Belief:

Today I Am Attracting (Write Down How Much Money You Are Attracting Today):

How Much Money Do I Plan On Spending Today (Write Down Your Imagined Amount)?

Based On My Response To The Previous Prompt, What Am I Spending My Money On?

Today I Am Investing My Money In:

For Every Dollar I Spend, How Much Of It Comes Back To Me?

I Feel:

I Believe God Is:

Today I Am Open To:

Today I Am Telling My Money To:

Today I Am Repeating To Myself:

I Feel Good Knowing:

Morning Thoughts:

Spending My Billions

(Nightly Thoughts - See It And Believe It)

Today I Visualized:

I Am Free From:

Today I Gave Away (Write Down How Much Money You Imagined Giving Away Or Actually Gave Away):

How Much Money Grew On My Money Tree Today?

I Felt Good Holding In My Hand (Write Down The Imagined Dollar Amount):

What Did I Actually Spend My Money On Today?

Today I Created:

How Did It Feel To Spend The Amount Of Money That I Spent Today And Why Did I Feel This Way?

Today It Was Fun To:

Today I Am Grateful For:

Today I Acted As If:

Tonight's Thoughts:

There Are No Limits To The Amount Of Money I Can Make.

Today's Money Story

Spending My Billions

(Morning Thoughts - See It And Believe It)

Date:

Today's Money Belief:

Today I Am Attracting (Write Down How Much Money You Are Attracting Today):

How Much Money Do I Plan On Spending Today (Write Down Your Imagined Amount)?

Based On My Response To The Previous Prompt, What Am I Spending My Money On?

Today I Am Investing My Money In:

For Every Dollar I Spend, How Much Of It Comes Back To Me?

I Feel:

I Believe God Is:

Today I Am Open To:

Today I Am Telling My Money To:

Today I Am Repeating To Myself:

I Feel Good Knowing:

Morning Thoughts:

Spending My Billions
(Nightly Thoughts - See It And Believe It)

Today I Visualized:

I Am Free From:

Today I Gave Away (Write Down How Much Money You Imagined Giving Away Or Actually Gave Away):

How Much Money Grew On My Money Tree Today?

I Felt Good Holding In My Hand (Write Down The Imagined Dollar Amount):

What Did I Actually Spend My Money On Today?

Today I Created:

How Did It Feel To Spend The Amount Of Money That I Spent Today And Why Did I Feel This Way?

Today It Was Fun To:

Today I Am Grateful For:

Today I Acted As If:

Tonight's Thoughts:

Spending My Billions
(Morning Thoughts - See It And Believe It)

Date:

I Feel:

Today's Money Belief:

I Believe God Is:

Today I Am Attracting (Write Down How Much Money You Are Attracting Today):

Today I Am Open To:

How Much Money Do I Plan On Spending Today (Write Down Your Imagined Amount)?

Today I Am Telling My Money To:

Based On My Response To The Previous Prompt, What Am I Spending My Money On?

Today I Am Repeating To Myself:

Today I Am Investing My Money In:

I Feel Good Knowing:

For Every Dollar I Spend, How Much Of It Comes Back To Me?

Morning Thoughts:

Spending My Billions
(Nightly Thoughts - See It And Believe It)

Today I Visualized:

I Am Free From:

Today I Gave Away (Write Down How Much Money You Imagined Giving Away Or Actually Gave Away):

How Much Money Grew On My Money Tree Today?

I Felt Good Holding In My Hand (Write Down The Imagined Dollar Amount):

What Did I Actually Spend My Money On Today?

Today I Created:

How Did It Feel To Spend The Amount Of Money That I Spent Today And Why Did I Feel This Way?

Today It Was Fun To:

Today I Am Grateful For:

Today I Acted As If:

Tonight's Thoughts:

I Am Doing This.

Money Does Grow On Trees.

Spending My Billions
(Morning Thoughts - See It And Believe It)

Date:

Today's Money Belief:

Today I Am Attracting (Write Down How Much Money You Are Attracting Today):

How Much Money Do I Plan On Spending Today (Write Down Your Imagined Amount)?

Based On My Response To The Previous Prompt, What Am I Spending My Money On?

Today I Am Investing My Money In:

For Every Dollar I Spend, How Much Of It Comes Back To Me?

I Feel:

I Believe God Is:

Today I Am Open To:

Today I Am Telling My Money To:

Today I Am Repeating To Myself:

I Feel Good Knowing:

Morning Thoughts:

Spending My Billions
(Nightly Thoughts - See It And Believe It)

Today I Visualized:

I Am Free From:

Today I Gave Away (Write Down How Much Money You Imagined Giving Away Or Actually Gave Away):

How Much Money Grew On My Money Tree Today?

I Felt Good Holding In My Hand (Write Down The Imagined Dollar Amount):

What Did I Actually Spend My Money On Today?

Today I Created:

How Did It Feel To Spend The Amount Of Money That I Spent Today And Why Did I Feel This Way?

Today It Was Fun To:

Today I Am Grateful For:

Today I Acted As If:

Tonight's Thoughts:

Today's Money Story

My New Lifestyle....

Spending My Billions
(Morning Thoughts - See It And Believe It)

Date:

Today's Money Belief:

Today I Am Attracting (Write Down How Much Money You Are Attracting Today):

How Much Money Do I Plan On Spending Today (Write Down Your Imagined Amount)?

Based On My Response To The Previous Prompt, What Am I Spending My Money On?

Today I Am Investing My Money In:

For Every Dollar I Spend, How Much Of It Comes Back To Me?

I Feel:

I Believe God Is:

Today I Am Open To:

Today I Am Telling My Money To:

Today I Am Repeating To Myself:

I Feel Good Knowing:

Morning Thoughts:

Spending My Billions
(Nightly Thoughts - See It And Believe It)

Today I Visualized:

I Am Free From:

Today I Gave Away (Write Down How Much Money You Imagined Giving Away Or Actually Gave Away):

How Much Money Grew On My Money Tree Today?

I Felt Good Holding In My Hand (Write Down The Imagined Dollar Amount):

What Did I Actually Spend My Money On Today?

Today I Created:

How Did It Feel To Spend The Amount Of Money That I Spent Today And Why Did I Feel This Way?

Today It Was Fun To:

Today I Am Grateful For:

Today I Acted As If:

Tonight's Thoughts:

Let It Flow.

Today's Money Story

Spending My Billions
(Morning Thoughts - See It And Believe It)

Date:

Today's Money Belief:

Today I Am Attracting (Write Down How Much Money You Are Attracting Today):

How Much Money Do I Plan On Spending Today (Write Down Your Imagined Amount)?

Based On My Response To The Previous Prompt, What Am I Spending My Money On?

Today I Am Investing My Money In:

For Every Dollar I Spend, How Much Of It Comes Back To Me?

I Feel:

I Believe God Is:

Today I Am Open To:

Today I Am Telling My Money To:

Today I Am Repeating To Myself:

I Feel Good Knowing:

Morning Thoughts:

Spending My Billions

(Nightly Thoughts - See It And Believe It)

Today I Visualized:

I Am Free From:

Today I Gave Away (Write Down How Much Money You Imagined Giving Away Or Actually Gave Away):

How Much Money Grew On My Money Tree Today?

I Felt Good Holding In My Hand (Write Down The Imagined Dollar Amount):

What Did I Actually Spend My Money On Today?

Today I Created:

How Did It Feel To Spend The Amount Of Money That I Spent Today And Why Did I Feel This Way?

Today It Was Fun To:

Today I Am Grateful For:

Today I Acted As If:

Tonight's Thoughts:

Money Mindset Practice

Write A Letter To 5 Individuals Who Treat Money And Receive Money The Way You Would Like To.

I Am Worthy.

Spending My Billions

(Morning Thoughts - See It And Believe It)

Date:

Today's Money Belief:

Today I Am Attracting (Write Down How Much Money You Are Attracting Today):

How Much Money Do I Plan On Spending Today (Write Down Your Imagined Amount)?

Based On My Response To The Previous Prompt, What Am I Spending My Money On?

Today I Am Investing My Money In:

For Every Dollar I Spend, How Much Of It Comes Back To Me?

I Feel:

I Believe God Is:

Today I Am Open To:

Today I Am Telling My Money To:

Today I Am Repeating To Myself:

I Feel Good Knowing:

Morning Thoughts:

Spending My Billions
(Nightly Thoughts - See It And Believe It)

Today I Visualized:

I Am Free From:

Today I Gave Away (Write Down How Much Money You Imagined Giving Away Or Actually Gave Away):

How Much Money Grew On My Money Tree Today?

I Felt Good Holding In My Hand (Write Down The Imagined Dollar Amount):

What Did I Actually Spend My Money On Today?

Today I Created:

How Did It Feel To Spend The Amount Of Money That I Spent Today And Why Did I Feel This Way?

Today It Was Fun To:

Today I Am Grateful For:

Today I Acted As If:

Tonight's Thoughts:

Spending My Billions
(Morning Thoughts - See It And Believe It)

Date:

Today's Money Belief:

Today I Am Attracting (Write Down How Much Money You Are Attracting Today):

How Much Money Do I Plan On Spending Today (Write Down Your Imagined Amount)?

Based On My Response To The Previous Prompt, What Am I Spending My Money On?

Today I Am Investing My Money In:

For Every Dollar I Spend, How Much Of It Comes Back To Me?

I Feel:

I Believe God Is:

Today I Am Open To:

Today I Am Telling My Money To:

Today I Am Repeating To Myself:

I Feel Good Knowing:

Morning Thoughts:

Spending My Billions

(Nightly Thoughts - See It And Believe It)

Today I Visualized:

I Am Free From:

Today I Gave Away (Write Down How Much Money You Imagined Giving Away Or Actually Gave Away):

How Much Money Grew On My Money Tree Today?

I Felt Good Holding In My Hand (Write Down The Imagined Dollar Amount):

What Did I Actually Spend My Money On Today?

Today I Created:

How Did It Feel To Spend The Amount Of Money That I Spent Today And Why Did I Feel This Way?

Today It Was Fun To:

Today I Am Grateful For:

Today I Acted As If:

Tonight's Thoughts:

Today's Money Story

My Personal Money Thoughts

Spending My Billions
(Morning Thoughts - See It And Believe It)

Date:

I Feel:

Today's Money Belief:

I Believe God Is:

Today I Am Attracting (Write Down How Much Money You Are Attracting Today):

Today I Am Open To:

How Much Money Do I Plan On Spending Today (Write Down Your Imagined Amount)?

Today I Am Telling My Money To:

Based On My Response To The Previous Prompt, What Am I Spending My Money On?

Today I Am Repeating To Myself:

Today I Am Investing My Money In:

I Feel Good Knowing:

For Every Dollar I Spend, How Much Of It Comes Back To Me?

Morning Thoughts:

Spending My Billions
(Nightly Thoughts - See It And Believe It)

Today I Visualized:

I Am Free From:

Today I Gave Away (Write Down How Much Money You Imagined Giving Away Or Actually Gave Away):

How Much Money Grew On My Money Tree Today?

I Felt Good Holding In My Hand (Write Down The Imagined Dollar Amount):

What Did I Actually Spend My Money On Today?

Today I Created:

How Did It Feel To Spend The Amount Of Money That I Spent Today And Why Did I Feel This Way?

Today It Was Fun To:

Today I Am Grateful For:

Today I Acted As If:

Tonight's Thoughts:

I Am Breaking Free From <u>All</u> Negative Money Thoughts.

Today's Money Story

Spending My Billions
(Morning Thoughts - See It And Believe It)

Date:

Today's Money Belief:

Today I Am Attracting (Write Down How Much Money You Are Attracting Today):

How Much Money Do I Plan On Spending Today (Write Down Your Imagined Amount)?

Based On My Response To The Previous Prompt, What Am I Spending My Money On?

Today I Am Investing My Money In:

For Every Dollar I Spend, How Much Of It Comes Back To Me?

I Feel:

I Believe God Is:

Today I Am Open To:

Today I Am Telling My Money To:

Today I Am Repeating To Myself:

I Feel Good Knowing:

Morning Thoughts:

Spending My Billions
(Nightly Thoughts - See It And Believe It)

Today I Visualized:

I Am Free From:

Today I Gave Away (Write Down How Much Money You Imagined Giving Away Or Actually Gave Away):

How Much Money Grew On My Money Tree Today?

I Felt Good Holding In My Hand (Write Down The Imagined Dollar Amount):

What Did I Actually Spend My Money On Today?

Today I Created:

How Did It Feel To Spend The Amount Of Money That I Spent Today And Why Did I Feel This Way?

Today It Was Fun To:

Today I Am Grateful For:

Today I Acted As If:

Tonight's Thoughts:

Spending My Billions

(Morning Thoughts - See It And Believe It)

Date: | I Feel:

Today's Money Belief: | I Believe God Is:

Today I Am Attracting (Write Down How Much Money You Are Attracting Today): | Today I Am Open To:

How Much Money Do I Plan On Spending Today (Write Down Your Imagined Amount)? | Today I Am Telling My Money To:

Based On My Response To The Previous Prompt, What Am I Spending My Money On? | Today I Am Repeating To Myself:

Today I Am Investing My Money In: | I Feel Good Knowing:

For Every Dollar I Spend, How Much Of It Comes Back To Me? | Morning Thoughts:

Spending My Billions
(Nightly Thoughts - See It And Believe It)

Today I Visualized:

I Am Free From:

Today I Gave Away (Write Down How Much Money You Imagined Giving Away Or Actually Gave Away):

How Much Money Grew On My Money Tree Today?

I Felt Good Holding In My Hand (Write Down The Imagined Dollar Amount):

What Did I Actually Spend My Money On Today?

Today I Created:

How Did It Feel To Spend The Amount Of Money That I Spent Today And Why Did I Feel This Way?

Today It Was Fun To:

Today I Am Grateful For:

Today I Acted As If:

Tonight's Thoughts:

251

My Personal Money Thoughts

I Like To Play With Money By....

Spending My Billions
(Morning Thoughts - See It And Believe It)

Date:

Today's Money Belief:

Today I Am Attracting (Write Down How Much Money You Are Attracting Today):

How Much Money Do I Plan On Spending Today (Write Down Your Imagined Amount)?

Based On My Response To The Previous Prompt, What Am I Spending My Money On?

Today I Am Investing My Money In:

For Every Dollar I Spend, How Much Of It Comes Back To Me?

I Feel:

I Believe God Is:

Today I Am Open To:

Today I Am Telling My Money To:

Today I Am Repeating To Myself:

I Feel Good Knowing:

Morning Thoughts:

Spending My Billions

(Nightly Thoughts - See It And Believe It)

Today I Visualized:

I Am Free From:

Today I Gave Away (Write Down How Much Money You Imagined Giving Away Or Actually Gave Away):

How Much Money Grew On My Money Tree Today?

I Felt Good Holding In My Hand (Write Down The Imagined Dollar Amount):

What Did I Actually Spend My Money On Today?

Today I Created:

How Did It Feel To Spend The Amount Of Money That I Spent Today And Why Did I Feel This Way?

Today It Was Fun To:

Today I Am Grateful For:

Today I Acted As If:

Tonight's Thoughts:

Spending My Billions

(Morning Thoughts - See It And Believe It)

Date:

Today's Money Belief:

Today I Am Attracting (Write Down How Much Money You Are Attracting Today):

How Much Money Do I Plan On Spending Today (Write Down Your Imagined Amount)?

Based On My Response To The Previous Prompt, What Am I Spending My Money On?

Today I Am Investing My Money In:

For Every Dollar I Spend, How Much Of It Comes Back To Me?

I Feel:

I Believe God Is:

Today I Am Open To:

Today I Am Telling My Money To:

Today I Am Repeating To Myself:

I Feel Good Knowing:

Morning Thoughts:

Spending My Billions

(Nightly Thoughts - See It And Believe It)

Today I Visualized:

I Am Free From:

Today I Gave Away (Write Down How Much Money You Imagined Giving Away Or Actually Gave Away):

How Much Money Grew On My Money Tree Today?

I Felt Good Holding In My Hand (Write Down The Imagined Dollar Amount):

What Did I Actually Spend My Money On Today?

Today I Created:

How Did It Feel To Spend The Amount Of Money That I Spent Today And Why Did I Feel This Way?

Today It Was Fun To:

Today I Am Grateful For:

Today I Acted As If:

Tonight's Thoughts:

Spending My Billions

(Morning Thoughts - See It And Believe It)

Date:

Today's Money Belief:

Today I Am Attracting (Write Down How Much Money You Are Attracting Today):

How Much Money Do I Plan On Spending Today (Write Down Your Imagined Amount)?

Based On My Response To The Previous Prompt, What Am I Spending My Money On?

Today I Am Investing My Money In:

For Every Dollar I Spend, How Much Of It Comes Back To Me?

I Feel:

I Believe God Is:

Today I Am Open To:

Today I Am Telling My Money To:

Today I Am Repeating To Myself:

I Feel Good Knowing:

Morning Thoughts:

Spending My Billions
(Nightly Thoughts - See It And Believe It)

Today I Visualized:

I Am Free From:

Today I Gave Away (Write Down How Much Money You Imagined Giving Away Or Actually Gave Away):

How Much Money Grew On My Money Tree Today?

I Felt Good Holding In My Hand (Write Down The Imagined Dollar Amount):

What Did I Actually Spend My Money On Today?

Today I Created:

How Did It Feel To Spend The Amount Of Money That I Spent Today And Why Did I Feel This Way?

Today It Was Fun To:

Today I Am Grateful For:

Today I Acted As If:

Tonight's Thoughts:

Today's Money Story

My Personal Money Thoughts

God Meets All My Needs. I Am Not Afraid To Let Anything Go.

Money Mindset Practice

Write Down 3 Money Fears. Release These Fears By Speaking And Believing The Opposite Of Them. Once Done, Destroy These Fears Physically By Burning What You Wrote And Mentally By Repeating The Opposite Of These Fears.

Spending My Billions
(Morning Thoughts - See It And Believe It)

Date:

I Feel:

Today's Money Belief:

I Believe God Is:

Today I Am Attracting (Write Down How Much Money You Are Attracting Today):

Today I Am Open To:

How Much Money Do I Plan On Spending Today (Write Down Your Imagined Amount)?

Today I Am Telling My Money To:

Based On My Response To The Previous Prompt, What Am I Spending My Money On?

Today I Am Repeating To Myself:

Today I Am Investing My Money In:

I Feel Good Knowing:

For Every Dollar I Spend, How Much Of It Comes Back To Me?

Morning Thoughts:

Spending My Billions

(Nightly Thoughts - See It And Believe It)

Today I Visualized:

I Am Free From:

Today I Gave Away (Write Down How Much Money You Imagined Giving Away Or Actually Gave Away):

How Much Money Grew On My Money Tree Today?

I Felt Good Holding In My Hand (Write Down The Imagined Dollar Amount):

What Did I Actually Spend My Money On Today?

Today I Created:

How Did It Feel To Spend The Amount Of Money That I Spent Today And Why Did I Feel This Way?

Today It Was Fun To:

Today I Am Grateful For:

Today I Acted As If:

Tonight's Thoughts:

Spending My Billions
(Morning Thoughts - See It And Believe It)

Date:

Today's Money Belief:

Today I Am Attracting (Write Down How Much Money You Are Attracting Today):

How Much Money Do I Plan On Spending Today (Write Down Your Imagined Amount)?

Based On My Response To The Previous Prompt, What Am I Spending My Money On?

Today I Am Investing My Money In:

For Every Dollar I Spend, How Much Of It Comes Back To Me?

I Feel:

I Believe God Is:

Today I Am Open To:

Today I Am Telling My Money To:

Today I Am Repeating To Myself:

I Feel Good Knowing:

Morning Thoughts:

Spending My Billions
(Nightly Thoughts - See It And Believe It)

Today I Visualized:

I Am Free From:

Today I Gave Away (Write Down How Much Money You Imagined Giving Away Or Actually Gave Away):

How Much Money Grew On My Money Tree Today?

I Felt Good Holding In My Hand (Write Down The Imagined Dollar Amount):

What Did I Actually Spend My Money On Today?

Today I Created:

How Did It Feel To Spend The Amount Of Money That I Spent Today And Why Did I Feel This Way?

Today It Was Fun To:

Today I Am Grateful For:

Today I Acted As If:

Tonight's Thoughts:

Today's Money Story

My Personal Money Thoughts

I Spend Money With No Fears.

Today's Money Story

Spending My Billions
(Morning Thoughts - See It And Believe It)

Date:

I Feel:

Today's Money Belief:

I Believe God Is:

Today I Am Attracting (Write Down How Much Money You Are Attracting Today):

Today I Am Open To:

How Much Money Do I Plan On Spending Today (Write Down Your Imagined Amount)?

Today I Am Telling My Money To:

Based On My Response To The Previous Prompt, What Am I Spending My Money On?

Today I Am Repeating To Myself:

Today I Am Investing My Money In:

I Feel Good Knowing:

For Every Dollar I Spend, How Much Of It Comes Back To Me?

Morning Thoughts:

Spending My Billions
(Nightly Thoughts - See It And Believe It)

Today I Visualized:

I Am Free From:

Today I Gave Away (Write Down How Much Money You Imagined Giving Away Or Actually Gave Away):

How Much Money Grew On My Money Tree Today?

I Felt Good Holding In My Hand (Write Down The Imagined Dollar Amount):

What Did I Actually Spend My Money On Today?

Today I Created:

How Did It Feel To Spend The Amount Of Money That I Spent Today And Why Did I Feel This Way?

Today It Was Fun To:

Today I Am Grateful For:

Today I Acted As If:

Tonight's Thoughts:

Spending My Billions
(Morning Thoughts - See It And Believe It)

Date:

Today's Money Belief:

Today I Am Attracting (Write Down How Much Money You Are Attracting Today):

How Much Money Do I Plan On Spending Today (Write Down Your Imagined Amount)?

Based On My Response To The Previous Prompt, What Am I Spending My Money On?

Today I Am Investing My Money In:

For Every Dollar I Spend, How Much Of It Comes Back To Me?

I Feel:

I Believe God Is:

Today I Am Open To:

Today I Am Telling My Money To:

Today I Am Repeating To Myself:

I Feel Good Knowing:

Morning Thoughts:

Spending My Billions
(Nightly Thoughts - See It And Believe It)

Today I Visualized:

I Am Free From:

Today I Gave Away (Write Down How Much Money You Imagined Giving Away Or Actually Gave Away):

How Much Money Grew On My Money Tree Today?

I Felt Good Holding In My Hand (Write Down The Imagined Dollar Amount):

What Did I Actually Spend My Money On Today?

Today I Created:

How Did It Feel To Spend The Amount Of Money That I Spent Today And Why Did I Feel This Way?

Today It Was Fun To:

Today I Am Grateful For:

Today I Acted As If:

Tonight's Thoughts:

I Am Wealthy Because My God Is Wealthy.

Today's Money Story

Spending My Billions
(Morning Thoughts - See It And Believe It)

Date:

I Feel:

Today's Money Belief:

I Believe God Is:

Today I Am Attracting (Write Down How Much Money You Are Attracting Today):

Today I Am Open To:

How Much Money Do I Plan On Spending Today (Write Down Your Imagined Amount)?

Today I Am Telling My Money To:

Based On My Response To The Previous Prompt, What Am I Spending My Money On?

Today I Am Repeating To Myself:

Today I Am Investing My Money In:

I Feel Good Knowing:

For Every Dollar I Spend, How Much Of It Comes Back To Me?

Morning Thoughts:

Spending My Billions
(Nightly Thoughts - See It And Believe It)

Today I Visualized:

I Am Free From:

Today I Gave Away (Write Down How Much Money You Imagined Giving Away Or Actually Gave Away):

How Much Money Grew On My Money Tree Today?

I Felt Good Holding In My Hand (Write Down The Imagined Dollar Amount):

What Did I Actually Spend My Money On Today?

Today I Created:

How Did It Feel To Spend The Amount Of Money That I Spent Today And Why Did I Feel This Way?

Today It Was Fun To:

Today I Am Grateful For:

Today I Acted As If:

Tonight's Thoughts:

Spending My Billions
(Morning Thoughts - See It And Believe It)

Date:

I Feel:

Today's Money Belief:

I Believe God Is:

Today I Am Attracting (Write Down How Much Money You Are Attracting Today):

Today I Am Open To:

How Much Money Do I Plan On Spending Today (Write Down Your Imagined Amount)?

Today I Am Telling My Money To:

Based On My Response To The Previous Prompt, What Am I Spending My Money On?

Today I Am Repeating To Myself:

Today I Am Investing My Money In:

I Feel Good Knowing:

For Every Dollar I Spend, How Much Of It Comes Back To Me?

Morning Thoughts:

Spending My Billions
(Nightly Thoughts - See It And Believe It)

Today I Visualized:

I Am Free From:

Today I Gave Away (Write Down How Much Money You Imagined Giving Away Or Actually Gave Away):

How Much Money Grew On My Money Tree Today?

I Felt Good Holding In My Hand (Write Down The Imagined Dollar Amount):

What Did I Actually Spend My Money On Today?

Today I Created:

How Did It Feel To Spend The Amount Of Money That I Spent Today And Why Did I Feel This Way?

Today It Was Fun To:

Today I Am Grateful For:

Today I Acted As If:

Tonight's Thoughts:

I Have The Power To Attract All The Money I Want.

It Feels Good To Spend Money.

Spending My Billions
(Morning Thoughts - See It And Believe It)

Date:

I Feel:

Today's Money Belief:

I Believe God Is:

Today I Am Attracting (Write Down How Much Money You Are Attracting Today):

Today I Am Open To:

How Much Money Do I Plan On Spending Today (Write Down Your Imagined Amount)?

Today I Am Telling My Money To:

Based On My Response To The Previous Prompt, What Am I Spending My Money On?

Today I Am Repeating To Myself:

Today I Am Investing My Money In:

I Feel Good Knowing:

For Every Dollar I Spend, How Much Of It Comes Back To Me?

Morning Thoughts:

Spending My Billions
(Nightly Thoughts - See It And Believe It)

Today I Visualized:

I Am Free From:

Today I Gave Away (Write Down How Much Money You Imagined Giving Away Or Actually Gave Away):

How Much Money Grew On My Money Tree Today?

I Felt Good Holding In My Hand (Write Down The Imagined Dollar Amount):

What Did I Actually Spend My Money On Today?

Today I Created:

How Did It Feel To Spend The Amount Of Money That I Spent Today And Why Did I Feel This Way?

Today It Was Fun To:

Today I Am Grateful For:

Today I Acted As If:

Tonight's Thoughts:

Today's Money Story

Great Things Do Happen To Me.

Spending My Billions

(Morning Thoughts - See It And Believe It)

Date:	I Feel:
Today's Money Belief:	I Believe God Is:
Today I Am Attracting (Write Down How Much Money You Are Attracting Today):	Today I Am Open To:
How Much Money Do I Plan On Spending Today (Write Down Your Imagined Amount)?	Today I Am Telling My Money To:
Based On My Response To The Previous Prompt, What Am I Spending My Money On?	Today I Am Repeating To Myself:
Today I Am Investing My Money In:	I Feel Good Knowing:
For Every Dollar I Spend, How Much Of It Comes Back To Me?	Morning Thoughts:

Spending My Billions
(Nightly Thoughts - See It And Believe It)

Today I Visualized:

I Am Free From:

Today I Gave Away (Write Down How Much Money You Imagined Giving Away Or Actually Gave Away):

How Much Money Grew On My Money Tree Today?

I Felt Good Holding In My Hand (Write Down The Imagined Dollar Amount):

What Did I Actually Spend My Money On Today?

Today I Created:

How Did It Feel To Spend The Amount Of Money That I Spent Today And Why Did I Feel This Way?

Today It Was Fun To:

Today I Am Grateful For:

Today I Acted As If:

Tonight's Thoughts:

I Like To Create....

Today's Money Story

Spending My Billions
(Morning Thoughts - See It And Believe It)

Date:

Today's Money Belief:

Today I Am Attracting (Write Down How Much Money You Are Attracting Today):

How Much Money Do I Plan On Spending Today (Write Down Your Imagined Amount)?

Based On My Response To The Previous Prompt, What Am I Spending My Money On?

Today I Am Investing My Money In:

For Every Dollar I Spend, How Much Of It Comes Back To Me?

I Feel:

I Believe God Is:

Today I Am Open To:

Today I Am Telling My Money To:

Today I Am Repeating To Myself:

I Feel Good Knowing:

Morning Thoughts:

Spending My Billions
(Nightly Thoughts - See It And Believe It)

Today I Visualized:

I Am Free From:

Today I Gave Away (Write Down How Much Money You Imagined Giving Away Or Actually Gave Away):

How Much Money Grew On My Money Tree Today?

I Felt Good Holding In My Hand (Write Down The Imagined Dollar Amount):

What Did I Actually Spend My Money On Today?

Today I Created:

How Did It Feel To Spend The Amount Of Money That I Spent Today And Why Did I Feel This Way?

Today It Was Fun To:

Today I Am Grateful For:

Today I Acted As If:

Tonight's Thoughts:

Spending My Billions
(Morning Thoughts - See It And Believe It)

Date:	I Feel:
Today's Money Belief:	I Believe God Is:
Today I Am Attracting (Write Down How Much Money You Are Attracting Today):	Today I Am Open To:
How Much Money Do I Plan On Spending Today (Write Down Your Imagined Amount)?	Today I Am Telling My Money To:
Based On My Response To The Previous Prompt, What Am I Spending My Money On?	Today I Am Repeating To Myself:
Today I Am Investing My Money In:	I Feel Good Knowing:
For Every Dollar I Spend, How Much Of It Comes Back To Me?	Morning Thoughts:

Spending My Billions
(Nightly Thoughts - See It And Believe It)

Today I Visualized:

I Am Free From:

Today I Gave Away (Write Down How Much Money You Imagined Giving Away Or Actually Gave Away):

How Much Money Grew On My Money Tree Today?

I Felt Good Holding In My Hand (Write Down The Imagined Dollar Amount):

What Did I Actually Spend My Money On Today?

Today I Created:

How Did It Feel To Spend The Amount Of Money That I Spent Today And Why Did I Feel This Way?

Today It Was Fun To:

Today I Am Grateful For:

Today I Acted As If:

Tonight's Thoughts:

Everyday Is An Amazing Day For Me.

I Am Wealthy Right Now.

Spending My Billions
(Morning Thoughts - See It And Believe It)

Date:

I Feel:

Today's Money Belief:

I Believe God Is:

Today I Am Attracting (Write Down How Much Money You Are Attracting Today):

Today I Am Open To:

How Much Money Do I Plan On Spending Today (Write Down Your Imagined Amount)?

Today I Am Telling My Money To:

Based On My Response To The Previous Prompt, What Am I Spending My Money On?

Today I Am Repeating To Myself:

Today I Am Investing My Money In:

I Feel Good Knowing:

For Every Dollar I Spend, How Much Of It Comes Back To Me?

Morning Thoughts:

Spending My Billions
(Nightly Thoughts - See It And Believe It)

Today I Visualized:

I Am Free From:

Today I Gave Away (Write Down How Much Money You Imagined Giving Away Or Actually Gave Away):

How Much Money Grew On My Money Tree Today?

I Felt Good Holding In My Hand (Write Down The Imagined Dollar Amount):

What Did I Actually Spend My Money On Today?

Today I Created:

How Did It Feel To Spend The Amount Of Money That I Spent Today And Why Did I Feel This Way?

Today It Was Fun To:

Today I Am Grateful For:

Today I Acted As If:

Tonight's Thoughts:

Today's Money Story

My Pockets Stay On Overflow.

Spending My Billions
(Morning Thoughts - See It And Believe It)

Date:

Today's Money Belief:

Today I Am Attracting (Write Down How Much Money You Are Attracting Today):

How Much Money Do I Plan On Spending Today (Write Down Your Imagined Amount)?

Based On My Response To The Previous Prompt, What Am I Spending My Money On?

Today I Am Investing My Money In:

For Every Dollar I Spend, How Much Of It Comes Back To Me?

I Feel:

I Believe God Is:

Today I Am Open To:

Today I Am Telling My Money To:

Today I Am Repeating To Myself:

I Feel Good Knowing:

Morning Thoughts:

Spending My Billions
(Nightly Thoughts - See It And Believe It)

Today I Visualized:

I Am Free From:

Today I Gave Away (Write Down How Much Money You Imagined Giving Away Or Actually Gave Away):

How Much Money Grew On My Money Tree Today?

I Felt Good Holding In My Hand (Write Down The Imagined Dollar Amount):

What Did I Actually Spend My Money On Today?

Today I Created:

How Did It Feel To Spend The Amount Of Money That I Spent Today And Why Did I Feel This Way?

Today It Was Fun To:

Today I Am Grateful For:

Today I Acted As If:

Tonight's Thoughts:

Whatever I Claim For Myself, I Can Get.

Today's Money Story

Spending My Billions
(Morning Thoughts - See It And Believe It)

Date:

Today's Money Belief:

Today I Am Attracting (Write Down
How Much Money You Are Attracting
Today):

How Much Money Do I Plan On
Spending Today (Write Down Your
Imagined Amount)?

Based On My Response To The
Previous Prompt, What Am I Spending
My Money On?

Today I Am Investing My Money In:

For Every Dollar I Spend, How Much Of
It Comes Back To Me?

I Feel:

I Believe God Is:

Today I Am Open To:

Today I Am Telling My Money To:

Today I Am Repeating To Myself:

I Feel Good Knowing:

Morning Thoughts:

Spending My Billions

(Nightly Thoughts - See It And Believe It)

Today I Visualized:

I Am Free From:

Today I Gave Away (Write Down How Much Money You Imagined Giving Away Or Actually Gave Away):

How Much Money Grew On My Money Tree Today?

I Felt Good Holding In My Hand (Write Down The Imagined Dollar Amount):

What Did I Actually Spend My Money On Today?

Today I Created:

How Did It Feel To Spend The Amount Of Money That I Spent Today And Why Did I Feel This Way?

Today It Was Fun To:

Today I Am Grateful For:

Today I Acted As If:

Tonight's Thoughts:

Spending My Billions
(Morning Thoughts - See It And Believe It)

Date:

Today's Money Belief:

Today I Am Attracting (Write Down
How Much Money You Are Attracting
Today):

How Much Money Do I Plan On
Spending Today (Write Down Your
Imagined Amount)?

Based On My Response To The
Previous Prompt, What Am I Spending
My Money On?

Today I Am Investing My Money In:

For Every Dollar I Spend, How Much Of
It Comes Back To Me?

I Feel:

I Believe God Is:

Today I Am Open To:

Today I Am Telling My Money To:

Today I Am Repeating To Myself:

I Feel Good Knowing:

Morning Thoughts:

Spending My Billions
(Nightly Thoughts - See It And Believe It)

Today I Visualized:

I Am Free From:

Today I Gave Away (Write Down How Much Money You Imagined Giving Away Or Actually Gave Away):

How Much Money Grew On My Money Tree Today?

I Felt Good Holding In My Hand (Write Down The Imagined Dollar Amount):

What Did I Actually Spend My Money On Today?

Today I Created:

How Did It Feel To Spend The Amount Of Money That I Spent Today And Why Did I Feel This Way?

Today It Was Fun To:

Today I Am Grateful For:

Today I Acted As If:

Tonight's Thoughts:

Spending My Billions
(Morning Thoughts - See It And Believe It)

Date:

Today's Money Belief:

Today I Am Attracting (Write Down How Much Money You Are Attracting Today):

How Much Money Do I Plan On Spending Today (Write Down Your Imagined Amount)?

Based On My Response To The Previous Prompt, What Am I Spending My Money On?

Today I Am Investing My Money In:

For Every Dollar I Spend, How Much Of It Comes Back To Me?

I Feel:

I Believe God Is:

Today I Am Open To:

Today I Am Telling My Money To:

Today I Am Repeating To Myself:

I Feel Good Knowing:

Morning Thoughts:

Spending My Billions
(Nightly Thoughts - See It And Believe It)

Today I Visualized:

I Am Free From:

Today I Gave Away (Write Down How Much Money You Imagined Giving Away Or Actually Gave Away):

How Much Money Grew On My Money Tree Today?

I Felt Good Holding In My Hand (Write Down The Imagined Dollar Amount):

What Did I Actually Spend My Money On Today?

Today I Created:

How Did It Feel To Spend The Amount Of Money That I Spent Today And Why Did I Feel This Way?

Today It Was Fun To:

Today I Am Grateful For:

Today I Acted As If:

Tonight's Thoughts:

311

My Personal Money Thoughts

Money Comes To Me Instantly.

Spending My Billions
(Morning Thoughts - See It And Believe It)

Date: | I Feel:

Today's Money Belief: | I Believe God Is:

Today I Am Attracting (Write Down How Much Money You Are Attracting Today): | Today I Am Open To:

How Much Money Do I Plan On Spending Today (Write Down Your Imagined Amount)? | Today I Am Telling My Money To:

Based On My Response To The Previous Prompt, What Am I Spending My Money On? | Today I Am Repeating To Myself:

Today I Am Investing My Money In: | I Feel Good Knowing:

For Every Dollar I Spend, How Much Of It Comes Back To Me? | Morning Thoughts:

Spending My Billions
(Nightly Thoughts - See It And Believe It)

Today I Visualized:

I Am Free From:

Today I Gave Away (Write Down How Much Money You Imagined Giving Away Or Actually Gave Away):

How Much Money Grew On My Money Tree Today?

I Felt Good Holding In My Hand (Write Down The Imagined Dollar Amount):

What Did I Actually Spend My Money On Today?

Today I Created:

How Did It Feel To Spend The Amount Of Money That I Spent Today And Why Did I Feel This Way?

Today It Was Fun To:

Today I Am Grateful For:

Today I Acted As If:

Tonight's Thoughts:

Spending My Billions
(Morning Thoughts - See It And Believe It)

Date:

Today's Money Belief:

Today I Am Attracting (Write Down How Much Money You Are Attracting Today):

How Much Money Do I Plan On Spending Today (Write Down Your Imagined Amount)?

Based On My Response To The Previous Prompt, What Am I Spending My Money On?

Today I Am Investing My Money In:

For Every Dollar I Spend, How Much Of It Comes Back To Me?

I Feel:

I Believe God Is:

Today I Am Open To:

Today I Am Telling My Money To:

Today I Am Repeating To Myself:

I Feel Good Knowing:

Morning Thoughts:

Spending My Billions
(Nightly Thoughts - See It And Believe It)

Today I Visualized:

I Am Free From:

Today I Gave Away (Write Down How Much Money You Imagined Giving Away Or Actually Gave Away):

How Much Money Grew On My Money Tree Today?

I Felt Good Holding In My Hand (Write Down The Imagined Dollar Amount):

What Did I Actually Spend My Money On Today?

Today I Created:

How Did It Feel To Spend The Amount Of Money That I Spent Today And Why Did I Feel This Way?

Today It Was Fun To:

Today I Am Grateful For:

Today I Acted As If:

Tonight's Thoughts:

Today's Money Story

My Mindset Has Changed.

Spending My Billions
(Morning Thoughts - See It And Believe It)

Date:

Today's Money Belief:

Today I Am Attracting (Write Down How Much Money You Are Attracting Today):

How Much Money Do I Plan On Spending Today (Write Down Your Imagined Amount)?

Based On My Response To The Previous Prompt, What Am I Spending My Money On?

Today I Am Investing My Money In:

For Every Dollar I Spend, How Much Of It Comes Back To Me?

I Feel:

I Believe God Is:

Today I Am Open To:

Today I Am Telling My Money To:

Today I Am Repeating To Myself:

I Feel Good Knowing:

Morning Thoughts:

Spending My Billions
(Nightly Thoughts - See It And Believe It)

Today I Visualized:

I Am Free From:

Today I Gave Away (Write Down How Much Money You Imagined Giving Away Or Actually Gave Away):

How Much Money Grew On My Money Tree Today?

I Felt Good Holding In My Hand (Write Down The Imagined Dollar Amount):

What Did I Actually Spend My Money On Today?

Today I Created:

How Did It Feel To Spend The Amount Of Money That I Spent Today And Why Did I Feel This Way?

Today It Was Fun To:

Today I Am Grateful For:

Today I Acted As If:

Tonight's Thoughts:

If I Want It, I Get It.

Today's Money Story

Spending My Billions
(Morning Thoughts - See It And Believe It)

Date:

Today's Money Belief:

Today I Am Attracting (Write Down How Much Money You Are Attracting Today):

How Much Money Do I Plan On Spending Today (Write Down Your Imagined Amount)?

Based On My Response To The Previous Prompt, What Am I Spending My Money On?

Today I Am Investing My Money In:

For Every Dollar I Spend, How Much Of It Comes Back To Me?

I Feel:

I Believe God Is:

Today I Am Open To:

Today I Am Telling My Money To:

Today I Am Repeating To Myself:

I Feel Good Knowing:

Morning Thoughts:

Spending My Billions

(Nightly Thoughts - See It And Believe It)

Today I Visualized:

I Am Free From:

Today I Gave Away (Write Down How Much Money You Imagined Giving Away Or Actually Gave Away):

How Much Money Grew On My Money Tree Today?

I Felt Good Holding In My Hand (Write Down The Imagined Dollar Amount):

What Did I Actually Spend My Money On Today?

Today I Created:

How Did It Feel To Spend The Amount Of Money That I Spent Today And Why Did I Feel This Way?

Today It Was Fun To:

Today I Am Grateful For:

Today I Acted As If:

Tonight's Thoughts:

Spending My Billions
(Morning Thoughts - See It And Believe It)

Date:

I Feel:

Today's Money Belief:

I Believe God Is:

Today I Am Attracting (Write Down How Much Money You Are Attracting Today):

Today I Am Open To:

How Much Money Do I Plan On Spending Today (Write Down Your Imagined Amount)?

Today I Am Telling My Money To:

Based On My Response To The Previous Prompt, What Am I Spending My Money On?

Today I Am Repeating To Myself:

Today I Am Investing My Money In:

I Feel Good Knowing:

For Every Dollar I Spend, How Much Of It Comes Back To Me?

Morning Thoughts:

Spending My Billions
(Nightly Thoughts - See It And Believe It)

Today I Visualized:

I Am Free From:

Today I Gave Away (Write Down How Much Money You Imagined Giving Away Or Actually Gave Away):

How Much Money Grew On My Money Tree Today?

I Felt Good Holding In My Hand (Write Down The Imagined Dollar Amount):

What Did I Actually Spend My Money On Today?

Today I Created:

How Did It Feel To Spend The Amount Of Money That I Spent Today And Why Did I Feel This Way?

Today It Was Fun To:

Today I Am Grateful For:

Today I Acted As If:

Tonight's Thoughts:

327

How Has My Money Language Changed?

All I Want Around Me Is Good. All I See Around Me Is Good.

Spending My Billions
(Morning Thoughts - See It And Believe It)

Date:

Today's Money Belief:

Today I Am Attracting (Write Down How Much Money You Are Attracting Today):

How Much Money Do I Plan On Spending Today (Write Down Your Imagined Amount)?

Based On My Response To The Previous Prompt, What Am I Spending My Money On?

Today I Am Investing My Money In:

For Every Dollar I Spend, How Much Of It Comes Back To Me?

I Feel:

I Believe God Is:

Today I Am Open To:

Today I Am Telling My Money To:

Today I Am Repeating To Myself:

I Feel Good Knowing:

Morning Thoughts:

Spending My Billions
(Nightly Thoughts - See It And Believe It)

Today I Visualized:

I Am Free From:

Today I Gave Away (Write Down How Much Money You Imagined Giving Away Or Actually Gave Away):

How Much Money Grew On My Money Tree Today?

I Felt Good Holding In My Hand (Write Down The Imagined Dollar Amount):

What Did I Actually Spend My Money On Today?

Today I Created:

How Did It Feel To Spend The Amount Of Money That I Spent Today And Why Did I Feel This Way?

Today It Was Fun To:

Today I Am Grateful For:

Today I Acted As If:

Tonight's Thoughts:

All Things Come Into My Life For My Greater Good.

The Doors I Knock On Open For Me.

Spending My Billions

(Morning Thoughts - See It And Believe It)

Date:

I Feel:

Today's Money Belief:

I Believe God Is:

Today I Am Attracting (Write Down How Much Money You Are Attracting Today):

Today I Am Open To:

How Much Money Do I Plan On Spending Today (Write Down Your Imagined Amount)?

Today I Am Telling My Money To:

Based On My Response To The Previous Prompt, What Am I Spending My Money On?

Today I Am Repeating To Myself:

Today I Am Investing My Money In:

I Feel Good Knowing:

For Every Dollar I Spend, How Much Of It Comes Back To Me?

Morning Thoughts:

Spending My Billions

(Nightly Thoughts - See It And Believe It)

Today I Visualized:

I Am Free From:

Today I Gave Away (Write Down How Much Money You Imagined Giving Away Or Actually Gave Away):

How Much Money Grew On My Money Tree Today?

I Felt Good Holding In My Hand (Write Down The Imagined Dollar Amount):

What Did I Actually Spend My Money On Today?

Today I Created:

How Did It Feel To Spend The Amount Of Money That I Spent Today And Why Did I Feel This Way?

Today It Was Fun To:

Today I Am Grateful For:

Today I Acted As If:

Tonight's Thoughts:

Today's Money Story

My Personal Money Thoughts

Spending My Billions
(Morning Thoughts - See It And Believe It)

Date:

Today's Money Belief:

Today I Am Attracting (Write Down How Much Money You Are Attracting Today):

How Much Money Do I Plan On Spending Today (Write Down Your Imagined Amount)?

Based On My Response To The Previous Prompt, What Am I Spending My Money On?

Today I Am Investing My Money In:

For Every Dollar I Spend, How Much Of It Comes Back To Me?

I Feel:

I Believe God Is:

Today I Am Open To:

Today I Am Telling My Money To:

Today I Am Repeating To Myself:

I Feel Good Knowing:

Morning Thoughts:

338

Spending My Billions
(Nightly Thoughts - See It And Believe It)

Today I Visualized:

I Am Free From:

Today I Gave Away (Write Down How Much Money You Imagined Giving Away Or Actually Gave Away):

How Much Money Grew On My Money Tree Today?

I Felt Good Holding In My Hand (Write Down The Imagined Dollar Amount):

What Did I Actually Spend My Money On Today?

Today I Created:

How Did It Feel To Spend The Amount Of Money That I Spent Today And Why Did I Feel This Way?

Today It Was Fun To:

Today I Am Grateful For:

Today I Acted As If:

Tonight's Thoughts:

And Whatever Things You Ask In Prayer, Believing, You Will Receive.

– Matthew 21:22

Today's Money Story

Spending My Billions
(Morning Thoughts - See It And Believe It)

Date: | I Feel:

Today's Money Belief: | I Believe God Is:

Today I Am Attracting (Write Down How Much Money You Are Attracting Today): | Today I Am Open To:

How Much Money Do I Plan On Spending Today (Write Down Your Imagined Amount)? | Today I Am Telling My Money To:

Based On My Response To The Previous Prompt, What Am I Spending My Money On? | Today I Am Repeating To Myself:

Today I Am Investing My Money In: | I Feel Good Knowing:

For Every Dollar I Spend, How Much Of It Comes Back To Me? | Morning Thoughts:

Spending My Billions
(Nightly Thoughts - See It And Believe It)

Today I Visualized:

I Am Free From:

Today I Gave Away (Write Down How Much Money You Imagined Giving Away Or Actually Gave Away):

How Much Money Grew On My Money Tree Today?

I Felt Good Holding In My Hand (Write Down The Imagined Dollar Amount):

What Did I Actually Spend My Money On Today?

Today I Created:

How Did It Feel To Spend The Amount Of Money That I Spent Today And Why Did I Feel This Way?

Today It Was Fun To:

Today I Am Grateful For:

Today I Acted As If:

Tonight's Thoughts:

Spending My Billions

(Morning Thoughts - See It And Believe It)

Date:

Today's Money Belief:

Today I Am Attracting (Write Down How Much Money You Are Attracting Today):

How Much Money Do I Plan On Spending Today (Write Down Your Imagined Amount)?

Based On My Response To The Previous Prompt, What Am I Spending My Money On?

Today I Am Investing My Money In:

For Every Dollar I Spend, How Much Of It Comes Back To Me?

I Feel:

I Believe God Is:

Today I Am Open To:

Today I Am Telling My Money To:

Today I Am Repeating To Myself:

I Feel Good Knowing:

Morning Thoughts:

Spending My Billions
(Nightly Thoughts - See It And Believe It)

Today I Visualized:

I Am Free From:

Today I Gave Away (Write Down How Much Money You Imagined Giving Away Or Actually Gave Away):

How Much Money Grew On My Money Tree Today?

I Felt Good Holding In My Hand (Write Down The Imagined Dollar Amount):

What Did I Actually Spend My Money On Today?

Today I Created:

How Did It Feel To Spend The Amount Of Money That I Spent Today And Why Did I Feel This Way?

Today It Was Fun To:

Today I Am Grateful For:

Today I Acted As If:

Tonight's Thoughts:

Spending My Billions
(Morning Thoughts - See It And Believe It)

Date:

Today's Money Belief:

Today I Am Attracting (Write Down
How Much Money You Are Attracting
Today):

How Much Money Do I Plan On
Spending Today (Write Down Your
Imagined Amount)?

Based On My Response To The
Previous Prompt, What Am I Spending
My Money On?

Today I Am Investing My Money In:

For Every Dollar I Spend, How Much Of
It Comes Back To Me?

I Feel:

I Believe God Is:

Today I Am Open To:

Today I Am Telling My Money To:

Today I Am Repeating To Myself:

I Feel Good Knowing:

Morning Thoughts:

Spending My Billions
(Nightly Thoughts - See It And Believe It)

Today I Visualized:

I Am Free From:

Today I Gave Away (Write Down How Much Money You Imagined Giving Away Or Actually Gave Away):

How Much Money Grew On My Money Tree Today?

I Felt Good Holding In My Hand (Write Down The Imagined Dollar Amount):

What Did I Actually Spend My Money On Today?

Today I Created:

How Did It Feel To Spend The Amount Of Money That I Spent Today And Why Did I Feel This Way?

Today It Was Fun To:

Today I Am Grateful For:

Today I Acted As If:

Tonight's Thoughts:

I Am Going To Be....

My Personal Money Thoughts

Spending My Billions
(Morning Thoughts - See It And Believe It)

Date:

Today's Money Belief:

Today I Am Attracting (Write Down
How Much Money You Are Attracting
Today):

How Much Money Do I Plan On
Spending Today (Write Down Your
Imagined Amount)?

Based On My Response To The
Previous Prompt, What Am I Spending
My Money On?

Today I Am Investing My Money In:

For Every Dollar I Spend, How Much Of
It Comes Back To Me?

I Feel:

I Believe God Is:

Today I Am Open To:

Today I Am Telling My Money To:

Today I Am Repeating To Myself:

I Feel Good Knowing:

Morning Thoughts:

Spending My Billions

(Nightly Thoughts - See It And Believe It)

Today I Visualized:

I Am Free From:

Today I Gave Away (Write Down How Much Money You Imagined Giving Away Or Actually Gave Away):

How Much Money Grew On My Money Tree Today?

I Felt Good Holding In My Hand (Write Down The Imagined Dollar Amount):

What Did I Actually Spend My Money On Today?

Today I Created:

How Did It Feel To Spend The Amount Of Money That I Spent Today And Why Did I Feel This Way?

Today It Was Fun To:

Today I Am Grateful For:

Today I Acted As If:

Tonight's Thoughts:

Spending My Billions
(Morning Thoughts - See It And Believe It)

Date:

I Feel:

Today's Money Belief:

I Believe God Is:

Today I Am Attracting (Write Down How Much Money You Are Attracting Today):

Today I Am Open To:

How Much Money Do I Plan On Spending Today (Write Down Your Imagined Amount)?

Today I Am Telling My Money To:

Based On My Response To The Previous Prompt, What Am I Spending My Money On?

Today I Am Repeating To Myself:

Today I Am Investing My Money In:

I Feel Good Knowing:

For Every Dollar I Spend, How Much Of It Comes Back To Me?

Morning Thoughts:

Spending My Billions

(Nightly Thoughts - See It And Believe It)

Today I Visualized:

I Am Free From:

Today I Gave Away (Write Down How Much Money You Imagined Giving Away Or Actually Gave Away):

How Much Money Grew On My Money Tree Today?

I Felt Good Holding In My Hand (Write Down The Imagined Dollar Amount):

What Did I Actually Spend My Money On Today?

Today I Created:

How Did It Feel To Spend The Amount Of Money That I Spent Today And Why Did I Feel This Way?

Today It Was Fun To:

Today I Am Grateful For:

Today I Acted As If:

Tonight's Thoughts:

Today's Money Story

Ask, And It Will Be Given To You; Seek, And You Will Find; Knock, And It Will Be Opened To You.

– Matthew 7:7

Spending My Billions
(Morning Thoughts - See It And Believe It)

Date:

I Feel:

Today's Money Belief:

I Believe God Is:

Today I Am Attracting (Write Down How Much Money You Are Attracting Today):

Today I Am Open To:

How Much Money Do I Plan On Spending Today (Write Down Your Imagined Amount)?

Today I Am Telling My Money To:

Based On My Response To The Previous Prompt, What Am I Spending My Money On?

Today I Am Repeating To Myself:

Today I Am Investing My Money In:

I Feel Good Knowing:

For Every Dollar I Spend, How Much Of It Comes Back To Me?

Morning Thoughts:

Spending My Billions

(Nightly Thoughts - See It And Believe It)

Today I Visualized:

I Am Free From:

Today I Gave Away (Write Down How Much Money You Imagined Giving Away Or Actually Gave Away):

How Much Money Grew On My Money Tree Today?

I Felt Good Holding In My Hand (Write Down The Imagined Dollar Amount):

What Did I Actually Spend My Money On Today?

Today I Created:

How Did It Feel To Spend The Amount Of Money That I Spent Today And Why Did I Feel This Way?

Today It Was Fun To:

Today I Am Grateful For:

Today I Acted As If:

Tonight's Thoughts:

Spending My Billions
(Morning Thoughts - See It And Believe It)

Date:

Today's Money Belief:

Today I Am Attracting (Write Down How Much Money You Are Attracting Today):

How Much Money Do I Plan On Spending Today (Write Down Your Imagined Amount)?

Based On My Response To The Previous Prompt, What Am I Spending My Money On?

Today I Am Investing My Money In:

For Every Dollar I Spend, How Much Of It Comes Back To Me?

I Feel:

I Believe God Is:

Today I Am Open To:

Today I Am Telling My Money To:

Today I Am Repeating To Myself:

I Feel Good Knowing:

Morning Thoughts:

Spending My Billions
(Nightly Thoughts - See It And Believe It)

Today I Visualized:

I Am Free From:

Today I Gave Away (Write Down How Much Money You Imagined Giving Away Or Actually Gave Away):

How Much Money Grew On My Money Tree Today?

I Felt Good Holding In My Hand (Write Down The Imagined Dollar Amount):

What Did I Actually Spend My Money On Today?

Today I Created:

How Did It Feel To Spend The Amount Of Money That I Spent Today And Why Did I Feel This Way?

Today It Was Fun To:

Today I Am Grateful For:

Today I Acted As If:

Tonight's Thoughts:

My Personal Money Thoughts

Money Mindset Practice

Create Your Own Bill And Write Down Who Would Be On It, How Much It Is Worth And What It Can Purchase.

Where Is My Money?

Today's Money Story

Spending My Billions
(Morning Thoughts - See It And Believe It)

Date:

Today's Money Belief:

Today I Am Attracting (Write Down How Much Money You Are Attracting Today):

How Much Money Do I Plan On Spending Today (Write Down Your Imagined Amount)?

Based On My Response To The Previous Prompt, What Am I Spending My Money On?

Today I Am Investing My Money In:

For Every Dollar I Spend, How Much Of It Comes Back To Me?

I Feel:

I Believe God Is:

Today I Am Open To:

Today I Am Telling My Money To:

Today I Am Repeating To Myself:

I Feel Good Knowing:

Morning Thoughts:

Spending My Billions
(Nightly Thoughts - See It And Believe It)

Today I Visualized:

I Am Free From:

Today I Gave Away (Write Down How Much Money You Imagined Giving Away Or Actually Gave Away):

How Much Money Grew On My Money Tree Today?

I Felt Good Holding In My Hand (Write Down The Imagined Dollar Amount):

What Did I Actually Spend My Money On Today?

Today I Created:

How Did It Feel To Spend The Amount Of Money That I Spent Today And Why Did I Feel This Way?

Today It Was Fun To:

Today I Am Grateful For:

Today I Acted As If:

Tonight's Thoughts:

Spending My Billions
(Morning Thoughts - See It And Believe It)

Date: | I Feel:

Today's Money Belief: | I Believe God Is:

Today I Am Attracting (Write Down How Much Money You Are Attracting Today): | Today I Am Open To:

How Much Money Do I Plan On Spending Today (Write Down Your Imagined Amount)? | Today I Am Telling My Money To:

Based On My Response To The Previous Prompt, What Am I Spending My Money On? | Today I Am Repeating To Myself:

Today I Am Investing My Money In: | I Feel Good Knowing:

For Every Dollar I Spend, How Much Of It Comes Back To Me? | Morning Thoughts:

Spending My Billions
(Nightly Thoughts - See It And Believe It)

Today I Visualized:

I Am Free From:

Today I Gave Away (Write Down How Much Money You Imagined Giving Away Or Actually Gave Away):

How Much Money Grew On My Money Tree Today?

I Felt Good Holding In My Hand (Write Down The Imagined Dollar Amount):

What Did I Actually Spend My Money On Today?

Today I Created:

How Did It Feel To Spend The Amount Of Money That I Spent Today And Why Did I Feel This Way?

Today It Was Fun To:

Today I Am Grateful For:

Today I Acted As If:

Tonight's Thoughts:

My Personal Money Thoughts

Jesus Said To Him, "If You Can Believe, All Things Are Possible To Him Who Believes."

–Mark 9:23

Spending My Billions
(Morning Thoughts - See It And Believe It)

Date:

I Feel:

Today's Money Belief:

I Believe God Is:

Today I Am Attracting (Write Down How Much Money You Are Attracting Today):

Today I Am Open To:

How Much Money Do I Plan On Spending Today (Write Down Your Imagined Amount)?

Today I Am Telling My Money To:

Based On My Response To The Previous Prompt, What Am I Spending My Money On?

Today I Am Repeating To Myself:

Today I Am Investing My Money In:

I Feel Good Knowing:

For Every Dollar I Spend, How Much Of It Comes Back To Me?

Morning Thoughts:

Spending My Billions
(Nightly Thoughts - See It And Believe It)

Today I Visualized:

I Am Free From:

Today I Gave Away (Write Down How Much Money You Imagined Giving Away Or Actually Gave Away):

How Much Money Grew On My Money Tree Today?

I Felt Good Holding In My Hand (Write Down The Imagined Dollar Amount):

What Did I Actually Spend My Money On Today?

Today I Created:

How Did It Feel To Spend The Amount Of Money That I Spent Today And Why Did I Feel This Way?

Today It Was Fun To:

Today I Am Grateful For:

Today I Acted As If:

Tonight's Thoughts:

Spending My Billions
(Morning Thoughts - See It And Believe It)

Date:

Today's Money Belief:

Today I Am Attracting (Write Down How Much Money You Are Attracting Today):

How Much Money Do I Plan On Spending Today (Write Down Your Imagined Amount)?

Based On My Response To The Previous Prompt, What Am I Spending My Money On?

Today I Am Investing My Money In:

For Every Dollar I Spend, How Much Of It Comes Back To Me?

I Feel:

I Believe God Is:

Today I Am Open To:

Today I Am Telling My Money To:

Today I Am Repeating To Myself:

I Feel Good Knowing:

Morning Thoughts:

Spending My Billions
(Nightly Thoughts - See It And Believe It)

Today I Visualized:

I Am Free From:

Today I Gave Away (Write Down How Much Money You Imagined Giving Away Or Actually Gave Away):

How Much Money Grew On My Money Tree Today?

I Felt Good Holding In My Hand (Write Down The Imagined Dollar Amount):

What Did I Actually Spend My Money On Today?

Today I Created:

How Did It Feel To Spend The Amount Of Money That I Spent Today And Why Did I Feel This Way?

Today It Was Fun To:

Today I Am Grateful For:

Today I Acted As If:

Tonight's Thoughts:

Today's Money Story

For As He Thinks In His Heart, So Is He.

– Proverbs 23:7

My Personal Money Thoughts

Today's Money Story

Spending My Billions
(Morning Thoughts - See It And Believe It)

Date:

I Feel:

Today's Money Belief:

I Believe God Is:

Today I Am Attracting (Write Down How Much Money You Are Attracting Today):

Today I Am Open To:

How Much Money Do I Plan On Spending Today (Write Down Your Imagined Amount)?

Today I Am Telling My Money To:

Based On My Response To The Previous Prompt, What Am I Spending My Money On?

Today I Am Repeating To Myself:

Today I Am Investing My Money In:

I Feel Good Knowing:

For Every Dollar I Spend, How Much Of It Comes Back To Me?

Morning Thoughts:

Spending My Billions
(Nightly Thoughts - See It And Believe It)

Today I Visualized:

I Am Free From:

Today I Gave Away (Write Down How Much Money You Imagined Giving Away Or Actually Gave Away):

How Much Money Grew On My Money Tree Today?

I Felt Good Holding In My Hand (Write Down The Imagined Dollar Amount):

What Did I Actually Spend My Money On Today?

Today I Created:

How Did It Feel To Spend The Amount Of Money That I Spent Today And Why Did I Feel This Way?

Today It Was Fun To:

Today I Am Grateful For:

Today I Acted As If:

Tonight's Thoughts:

I Am Happy With Everything I Have And With Who I Am Becoming.

Made in the USA
Columbia, SC
15 August 2021

43705140R00228